EXPLORING
ICELAND´S GEOLOGY

SNÆBJÖRN GUÐMUNDSSON

EXPLORING ICELAND´S GEOLOGY

MÁL OG MENNING

Exploring Iceland's Geology
© Snæbjörn Guðmundsson 2015
English translation © Katrina Downs-Rose 2016

Mál og menning
Reykjavík 2019

All rights reserved.

Editor: Örn Sigurðsson
Maps: Hans H. Hansen, fixlanda.is
Layout: Guðjón Ingi Hauksson
Cover design: Halla Sigga / Forlagið
Printing: Almarose, Slovenia

Published in Reykjavík, a UNESCO City of Literature

1st edition 2016
Reprinted 2019

Photography:
Snævarr Guðmundsson and Shutterstock, except Guðmundur Páll Ólafsson
(p. 32, 36, 66, 82), Jóhann Ísberg (p. 140, 141, 142), Ómar Smári Kristinsson
(p. 44, 45), Ágúst Guðmundsson (p. 50), Einar Ragnar Sigurðsson (p. 35),
Guðjón Ingi Hauksson (p. 110) and Gunnar Sverrisson (p. 7).

Cover photo: Eldgjá

ISBN 978-9979-3-3625-9

Mál og menning is an imprint of ❦ Forlagið ehf.
www.forlagid.is

Index

Introduction

There is probably no need to tell visitors how geologically significant Iceland is, or how important it is to study the country's geology. Extensive research has of course been done in Iceland since the 19th century, by both Icelandic and overseas geologists, so a great deal of information has been collected, particularly in more recent years. Quite a lot of this knowledge has found its way into geology books, but for a long time a book has been needed for visitors, describing the geology of the whole land in an easily understandable and accessible manner.

It could be said that the material for this book is taken from the decades-long tireless work of many geologists, and the author's contribution has been limited to collecting it together and making it available for people who want to learn about the country's geology. The book explores the geology of 50 destinations or natural phenomena in Iceland that should be of particular interest to people touring the country. It is not intended as a reference book or academic text. Instead, the book has short geological descriptions about things that the author finds interesting, and the chapters should provide a good picture of the geology of each place. Before embarking on a journey around Iceland it is necessary to have a good topographical map at hand, and the various geological maps that have been published are recommended too.

Some years ago, a young geology student at the University of Iceland asked a professor, "Why do people learn geology?" The professor thought for a while, and then replied, "So that it is more fun to travel around the country." The author of this book agrees wholeheartedly with this. Hopefully, the book will benefit readers travelling in Iceland and perhaps make the journey more enjoyable.

Snæbjörn Guðmundsson

Snæbjörn Guðmundsson is a geologist by training and has acquired an extensive knowledge of Iceland's geology and geological history. He has taught at the University of Iceland and actively promotes better public understanding of the country's exceptional geology.

Naustahvilft

Kálfshamarsvík

Dynjandi

Látrabjarg

Hvítserkur

Rauðasandur

Vatnsdalshólar

Snæfellsjökull

Eldborg

Hverave

Búðahraun

Grábrók

Hraunfossar and
Barnafoss

Kerlinga

Geysir and
Strokkur

Gullfoss

Þingvellir

Kerið and
Grímsnes

Þríhnúkagígur

Hekla

Land
la

Bláa lónið

Krýsuvík

Fimmvörðuháls

Eyjafjallajökull

Heimaey

Sólheima

Surtsey

Dyrhó

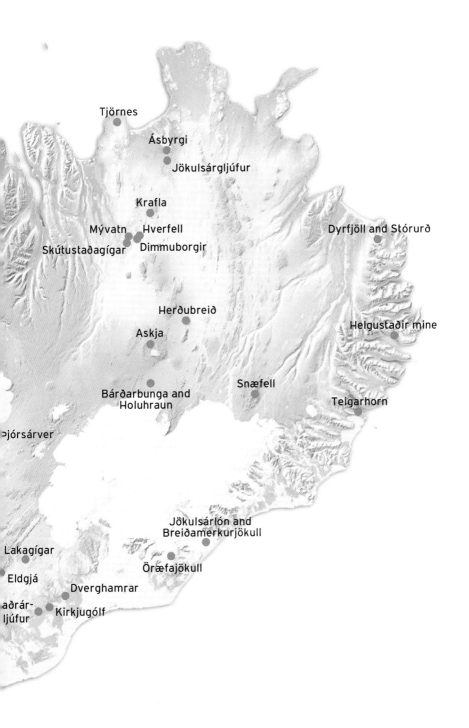

Tjörnes

Ásbyrgi

Jökulsárgljúfur

Krafla

Mývatn Hverfell

Skútustaðagígar Dimmuborgir

Dyrfjöll and Stórurð

Herðubreið

Askja

Helgustaðir mine

Snæfell

Bárðarbunga and
Holuhraun

Teigarhorn

Þjórsárver

Jökulsárlón and
Breiðamerkurjökull

Lakagígar

Eldgjá

Öræfajökull

Dverghamrar

aðrár-
ljúfur Kirkjugólf

The Formation of Iceland

Just after seven in the morning on 14 November 1963, Guðmar Tómasson, skipper on the fishing boat Ísleifur II, radioed Vestmannaeyjar Coast Guard and asked if there was a report of a boat in distress in the area south of the Vestmannaeyjar archipelago. Ísleifur II's crew had been fishing near the skerry Geirfuglasker, and one of them, Ólafur Vestmann, had noticed an enormous cloud of smoke rising from the ocean's surface some distance from the ship. The reply from the radio was that no emergency call had been received, but day was only just dawning and the crew were not sure what was happening on this otherwise calm morning. Consequently, the boat was slowly sailed close to the disturbance, soon worked out what was happening. The crew stopped the boat about half a nautical mile from the smoke and stared in astonishment at one of the most remarkable natural events anyone could hope to witness. An eruption had started on the seafloor, close to the boat, and the sea seethed while the column of smoke rose silently from the water's surface. Ísleifur II's crew thought it unwise to go closer, but continued to fish as if nothing had happened, about one nautical mile away from the commotion. Most people know the sequel – the eruption that had begun there continued intermittently for almost four years, and left behind a brand-new island, Surtsey. The Surtsey eruption was not only a special event in the eyes of the general public, it was also important to the world of geology. Submarine eruptions are very similar to subglacial ones, and the eruption confirmed geologist Guðmundur Kjartansson's theory that Iceland's tuyas (table mountains) formed beneath Ice Age glaciers. The eruption's behaviour was also an important subject for research, and explosive eruptions that occur in shallow water are now often named after Surtsey, so they are called Surtseyan eruptions. Finally, attention is drawn to the importance of research on the coastal erosion that has shaped Surtsey ever since its birth.

The question then arises, is this starting at the wrong end? Should a discussion of Iceland's geological history instead end with a description of the Surtsey eruption? Certainly the eruption was important for modern geology and our understanding of various natural processes, but at the same time it seems that few events have caused such a profound misunderstanding of Iceland's geological history. Ever since Surtsey erupted, many people have had the idea that Iceland's origin is exemplified in the Surtsey eruption, and that innumerable submarine eruptions built up and created the island of Iceland in the middle of the Atlantic Ocean. The idea that Iceland rose from the sea about 15-25 million years ago has even been repeated in many textbooks and geology books, right through to the present day. However, it has long been obvious that this is a persistent misconception because, if the geological history is studied from all angles, it can be seen that Iceland never emerged from the sea's surface – it has in fact been sticking out ever since the Atlantic Ocean began to form.

New crust at a plate boundary

Iceland's oldest rock is found on the promontories in the east and west of the country. On the northernmost tips of the West Fjords, such as Göltur at the mouth of Súgandafjörður, is rock that is about 15-16 million years old, and rock that is 1-2 million years younger can be found furthest east on the headland between Norðfjarðarflói and Reyðarfjörður. It is often said that Iceland is about 14-16 million years old – which is not wrong, but only one of many possible an-

swers when it comes to the question of Iceland's age. The formation of Iceland is closely connected to movements of the Earth's tectonic plates. With the rise of plate tectonic theory, and its acceptance in the latter half of the 20th century, it became clear that Iceland lies at the junction of the North American and Eurasian plates, two of the largest tectonic plates on Earth. Their junction is defined by, among other things, the northern part of the Mid-Atlantic Ridge, and Iceland is the only land mass of any real size on that part of the ridge. So it is possible to say that the Mid-Atlantic Ridge lies across the middle of Iceland, from Reykjanestá eastwards through south Iceland and the central highlands, over to the northwest part of Vatnajökull, and then north through Ódáðahraun to the coast at Tjörnes and Öxarfjörður.

At their junction, the tectonic plates move apart at about the equivalent of two centimetres a year, or around 20 km in a million years, and new rock is continually forming in eruptions along the plate boundary, while older rock is carried away from the middle of the country by the motion of the plates. It is quite easy to imagine that when the rocks in the West and East Fjords were forming at the plate junction in the middle of the land, then even older rock existed further out, at the edges of the land mass of that time. The older rock has disappeared into the sea now, but we can see signs of it in the vast continental shelf around Iceland. The land sinks into the sea away from the plate boundary, both as a result of erosion by sea, water or glacier, and also because when the newly formed, hot crust drifts away from the plate boundary it gradually cools. The rock in the crust and upper mantle, together called the lithosphere, contracts when it cools, and this increases the density of the rock so that it sinks down into the mantle. This process can be easily seen at the Earth's oceanic ridges where newly formed crust rises on the plate boundary itself and creates a high ridge, but the seafloor slopes rapidly away on either side because the rock sinks as it drifts away and cools. With this process in mind, it is obvious that there is no reason to assume that the oldest rock now found in Iceland marks the real start of the country. It could easily be that older rock, which is now below sea level, used to be on dry land.

How long has this process lasted though, in the area now covered by the North Atlantic? If we go back far enough in time, and undo the tectonic plate movements that constantly increase the distance between the coasts of Europe and Greenland, we finally reach the point in time when the continents were next to each other, and the North Atlantic did not exist. Before this time, North America and Eurasia lay together as one supercontinent called Laurasia; it was formed by plate tectonic processes earlier in Earth's history. At the margins of this plate there used to be vast fold-mountains that formed around 400 million years ago or more, and we can see the eroded remnants of the mountains either side of the North Atlantic now, for example in Norway. About 60 million years ago, extensive volcanic activity began in the region, and there are signs of this in the vast basalt formations on the east coast of Greenland, the Faroe Islands, and northern Scotland, for example. This volcanic activity marked the start of the separation of Greenland and northern Europe that we still see at work in

Iceland. As the continents move apart, hot rock flows from the mantle up to the lower crust where a tiny portion of it melts and migrates up to the surface as magma in a volcanic eruption. This volcanic activity creates what is called oceanic crust, which is made of basalt and usually both denser and thinner than the crust that forms the continents. The oldest oceanic crust in the North Atlantic between Greenland and Europe is about 54-56 million years old, and this suggests that divergence was well underway at this time in the region; the southern part of the Atlantic had already been opening for some tens of millions of years.

Hot spot and mantle plume

The divergence of tectonic plates in the North Atlantic is only one of two main reasons for the formation of Iceland. It has long been obvious that Iceland is on a "hot spot", an area where volcanic activity is unusually intense compared to other regions of the Earth, and there is more accumulation of volcanic rocks. This is demonstrated by Iceland's much higher position in comparison with the rest of the Atlantic Ridge than the rest of the Atlantic

Ridge, which in most places lies at a depth of about two or three kilometres in the sea. Although opinions differ about the cause of the hot spot, most geoscientists incline towards the theory that below Iceland there is a powerful mantle plume which rises hundreds of kilometres from deep in the earth's mantle. The mantle plume is not made of molten rock, rather it is best described as an up-flow of rock that is about 130–150°C hotter than the surrounding rock. This temperature difference is sufficient to allow magma production to begin at a greater depth than otherwise, and production is greater than in other places on the Mid-Atlantic Ridge. Activity appears at the surface as a hot spot. Research shows that the centre of the mantle plume is now almost directly below Bárðarbunga in Iceland's central highlands, but this has not always been the case. Although the mantle plume is thought to be virtually static, the tectonic plates forming the crust move over it, and the boundary between the North American and Eurasian plates moves slowly to the northwest, relative to the mantle plume. This means that the mantle plume appears to have moved southeast in geological time, relative to the plate boundary.

When divergence was beginning between Greenland and Northern Europe about 50–60 million years ago, the mantle plume was located some distance west of the plate boundary, probably under the middle of Greenland. Soon after divergence began, the sea flowed along the new plate boundary, and the North Atlantic was at first just a very narrow strip of sea between two continents, not unlike the Red Sea today. In the area around the mantle plume there was greater accretion than in other places on the plate boundary, and the crust there was thick enough to protrude of the newly formed ocean. This is an important event in the formation of Iceland because the North Atlantic widened as the millions of years passed, but part of the oceanic crust always stood out as a land bridge between Greenland and Northern Europe. This land bridge has now sunk into the sea, but we see signs of it in the shallow seas on either side of the country, both between Greenland and Iceland, and Iceland and the Faroe Islands. At the same time as the Atlantic widened, the divergent plate boundary always moved northwest relative to the mantle plume, and about 25 million years ago the plate boundary appears to have finally reached the mantle plume. Volcanic activity increased dramatically when the mantle plume and the plate boundary united, and the land mass that stood out of the ocean widened from south to north. We see indications of this event on the continental shelf around Iceland, which is much wider than the shallow submarine ridge between Iceland and the Faroe Islands – a large portion of the land which was formed in the last 20 million years has sunk into the sea.

The North Atlantic land bridge

So what indications are there that a land bridge was ever part of the geological history of the North Atlantic? Is it possible that the oceanic crust on either side of Iceland simply formed under the ocean, and the land emerged from the sea when volcanic activity increased at the same time as the plate boundary moved over the mantle plume? Answers to these speculations have come from many directions, and almost all of them point to the same conclusion – that Iceland was once part of a land bridge which extended right across the Atlantic. Firstly, research on the oceanic floor of the ridges west and east of Iceland has shown that their surface is widely covered by sloping lava formations, often hidden by thick sediments. The formations probably erupted above sea level and are very similar to the sloping lava formations in Iceland, which can be seen in the West Fjords and East Fjords. Secondly, geologists have also tried to estimate how much the crust on either side of Iceland has subsided since it was first formed at the plate boundary. About 280 km separates Greenland from Iceland now, and the maximum depth down to the Greenland-Iceland ridge is only about 600 m. The crust in this area cooled and subsided as it moved away from the plate boundary, and by estimating the rate of crustal subsidence it is possible to come close to knowing how long it has been since the ridge first sank below sea-level. Based on this, scientists believe that a land bridge to Greenland existed until about 10-18 million years ago. The same can be said about the Iceland-Faroe ridge, which is considerably longer at around 450 km and at a maximum depth of about 500 m – although there is a somewhat deeper bit of ridge east of the Faroe Islands. Geologists think that the Iceland-Faroe ridge first sank below sea level about 14-20 million years ago. From these numbers it can be assumed that a fairly continuous land bridge lay between Greenland and North Europe for the first 35–40 million years of the 55-million-year-long history of the North Atlantic.

This research provides clues about the development of Iceland, but in the field of geological palaeontology, it has proved even more useful when dating the North Atlantic land bridge. In old sedimentary layers in Iceland, various plant remains have been preserved, such as leaves, pinecones, seeds and needles, as well as pollen from many plant species. By identifying these fossilised remains, it is possible to examine how they are related to modern and ancient plant communities in North America, Europe and Asia. The oldest plant remains in Icelandic sediments are about 15 million years old, found on the outermost tips of the West Fjords, but obviously it is not easy to access older sediments since they

have subsided below sea level. As you go further inland towards the current plate boundary, sediments containing younger fossilised plants are found. Icelandic geologists have in recent years studied Iceland's ancient flora, placing considerable emphasis on looking at how plant species used to seed themselves and spread. When the oldest fossilised plants are examined, plants which lived in Iceland about 10-15 million years ago, most of them dispersed their seeds by wind. However, about 10% of the identified species used short-distance dispersal in which the seed is carried a short way by animals or by gravity, where the fruit or seed falls directly to ground from the plant. Examples of such plants include oak, beech and chestnut, and it is obvious that such plant species cannot distribute themselves across wide oceans: they have to spread by land. Their occurrence in old sediments in Iceland is therefore a sign of an accessible land bridge between Iceland and the continents. New plant species that used short-distance seed dispersal were still appearing in the Icelandic flora up until 6-7 million years ago; they were probably North American species. The youngest European species came to Iceland about 9-10 million years ago; after that, the land bridge to Europe was probably broken. By contrast, new plant species appearing in the Icelandic flora in the last six million years all use long-distance seed dispersal by wind or bird, suggesting that all overland routes between Iceland and the rest of the world had been cut, and the land bridge had sunk into the sea. Research in palaeontology suggests that a land bridge all the way from Greenland to Europe existed until about 9-10 million years ago, and from Greenland to Iceland for a few million years longer, although towards the end the land bridge was probably only a collection of islands.

Two almost conclusive bits of evidence

of the land bridge do exist though. In the summer of 1980 bones of a small species of deer were found in 3–3.5-million-year-old sediments at Bustarfell in Vopnafjörður, and they are the only fossilised land mammal remains of pre-glacial age that have been found in Iceland. It is fairly clear that land mammals did not travel to Iceland across the ocean; instead they came from the continents across a land bridge and later became trapped when Iceland became an island. About a million years before the Ice Age began, wildlife thrived in Iceland, and ancient plant remains show that the climate was much warmer in Iceland then. The strangest evidence for a land bridge was found almost twenty years after the Bustarfell discovery. In the summer of 1998, an Icelandic zoologist was researching stickleback fish in Lake Þingvallavatn when, by sheer chance, he caught a shrimp-like freshwater amphipod. Two years later more specimens were found, and as a result it was discovered that in Iceland there are two species of groundwater amphipods which nobody knew about or even expected find. Extensive studies of these amphipods have been made since then, and they are found all over the country, all the way from

the Ölfusá river estuary, north to Kópasker. And wherever they are found, they are in groundwater springs on the edges of young and unaltered lava flows. Research teams lead by biologists from the University of Iceland have studied the amphipods, their distribution and genetics. The research shows that one species of amphipod has only very distant relatives, but the other species is quite closely related to amphipods on both sides of the Atlantic Ocean, and the Icelandic and foreign species may have been separated from each other about 10–15 million years ago, or even earlier. Freshwater amphipods like these tolerate saltwater badly, if at all, so they cannot have been carried across the ocean. Instead, their existence here requires a land bridge earlier in Iceland's geological history. Since the amphipods arrived in Iceland by land bridge more than 10 million years ago they have survived repeated glaciations. At their largest, the Ice Age glaciers more or less covered all of Iceland, so it can be assumed that the amphipods survived beneath thick ice, probably in groundwater connected to a geothermal area. It is hardly possible to call it an exciting existence though – groundwater is only two to six degrees celsius, and the amphipods live off a bacterial film that they scrape from the surface of rocks in the water.

Iceland's geological history

As mentioned earlier, the oldest rocks in Iceland are can be found on the tips of headlands in the West Fjords and East Fjords, and they are about 14-16 million years old. The varied and interesting history of Iceland's formation before this period has almost completely vanished from sight, so it has to be deliberately uncovered, as in the previous chapter. The geological history after this time is more or less on display to us in different parts of Iceland, each with their own characteristics. Most of this book tells the geological story as it is disclosed to us when we travel around the country. On our journey, we must not forget that geology constantly calls on us to follow clues, even ones that seem not to fit, and it can often prove a challenging subject. So it is good to keep in mind the dynamic picture of Iceland that we have outlined here - where more or less all the rock is created at the plate boundary in the middle of the country, after which it moves gradually out to the edges, taking millions of years, and finally sinks into the sea.

Iceland is reminiscent of a conveyor-belt where the rock forms, moves and sinks. Most of the rock in the older parts of Iceland originally flowed as fresh new lava in active volcanic belts, but time and plate tectonics have treated it so harshly that most people are unable to tell that the rock was originally lava. About 12-15 million years ago the West Fjords may have looked like the modern-day areas of Reykjanes or Ódáðahraun, with vast lava fiows that had been layered on top of each other after magnificent volcanic eruptions. However, since the Ice Age did not begin in Iceland until about 3-5 million years ago, no mountains of móberg (hyaloclastite) rose from these old lava fields, and the gla-

cially eroded and dramatic landscapes now visible in the West Fjords and East Fjords were nowhere to be seen. In periods when no lava flowed, an iron-rich and fertile volcanic soil formed, and in it were buried plant fragments that have sometimes been preserved until the present day. In other words, we need to constantly dismiss from our minds the idea of how Iceland looks now, because the appearance of the landscape has been completely changed by erosion as to make it almost unrecognisable.

So how old is Iceland? What starting-point is aimed for when trying to decide the age of the country? In fact there is no single answer to these questions, and it is possible to consider several stages in the continuous history of the country, each of which could suggest a possible age for Iceland. It would be possible to start from the point of the island's birth of the land bridge when divergence originally began between Greenland and North Europe, about 54-56 million years ago. Around 23-25 million years ago the boundary between the European and North American plates drifted over the same mantle plume that we now find beneath the centre of Iceland. This increased the rate at which the landmass built up, so that it reached a similar size as Iceland today, and some people might want to count that as the beginning of Iceland. Or how about using the age of the oldest rock now found at the surface in Iceland? That is about 15-16 million years old, outermost on the headlands of the West Fjords. Finally, it would be possible to link Iceland's age to when the land bridge to Greenland finally broke, around 6-10 million years ago, after which Iceland finally stood as an island in the middle of the North Atlantic. Perhaps it is just simplest to leave the age of the country undecided. Is there really any need to divide a dynamic history like the geological formation of Iceland?

WEST

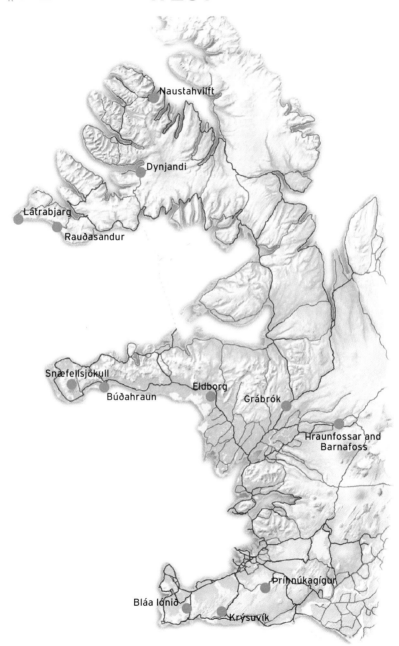

W

Naustahvilft

Dynjandi

Látrabjarg

Rauðasandur

Snæfellsjökull

Búðahraun

Eldborg

Grábrók

Hraunfossar and
Barnafoss

Þrímúkagígur

Bláa lónið

Krýsuvík

Bláa lónið

Bláa lónið, the Blue Lagoon, is Iceland's most popular tourist destination, and about 90% of all tourists visiting Iceland go there. The lagoon is known around the world for its beauty, as it lies curiously blue in the jet-black lava near Svartsengi. The Blue Lagoon's reputation is no less due to the properties of the bathing water; the water is rich in dissolved minerals and has a beneficial effect on various skin conditions. In geological terms the Blue Lagoon is special in many ways too. It is a discharge reservoir for the geothermal power plant at Svartsengi, so it is a man-made construction even though it looks like a natural feature in many ways. Maybe it is possible to class it as a man-made geological feature, along with hydroelectric reservoirs. However, unlike a hydroelectric reservoir, the Blue Lagoon is constantly advancing. Since the commissioning of the geothermal power plant in 1976, the lagoon has grown ever larger and inched its way further and further into the black lava each year.

In contrast to a hydroelectric reservoir, the Blue Lagoon is not a necessary part of the geothermal power plant at Svartsengi; rather it is a by-product of the plant's operation. Harnessing the high-temperature geothermal field at Svartsengi was begun in 1971 when the drilling of geothermal wells began. The first boreholes were only a few hundred metres deep but sizeable enough to provide around 200°C geothermal fluid for the production of hot water, and distribution of hot water from Svartsengi began in 1976. The geothermal fluid from Svartsengi is very rich in dissolved matter, and it is therefore very corrosive. As a result, it is impossible to use it directly to heat houses because the fluid would destroy the plumbing. Instead the fluid is used to heat freshwater, which is then pumped to municipal-

ities in the Suðurnes area. This is also the practice at other high-temperature areas, such as Nesjavellir.

Since the geothermal fluid is not used directly in houses, it is left behind after the production process. Immediately after commissioning of the plant in the mid-1970s, they began pumping the excess fluid out onto the lava field by the power plant. The lava that the Svartsengi power plant stands on is called Illahraun, and it is thought to have been erupted in 1226, from a short crater row just west of the Blue Lagoon. Because of its young age, the lava is unaltered and porous, and surface water seeps easily down through it. At first the discharge water from the power plant simply disappeared through the lava, into the bedrock. The fluid is, however, very rich in silica, and a large portion of the silica precipitates out of the water on cooling. This creates sludge in the water, which fills the cracks and pores in the lava, and a lake began to form where the run-off water flowed onto the lava soon after the power plant was commissioned. At first the lake was not very large, and probably few people would have thought of bathing in the scalding-hot and highly salty puddle.

It was not until late 1981 that Valur Margeirsson, a young man from Keflavík, started to bathe in the discharge water, with permission from the head of the district heating company Hitaveita Suðurnesja. Valur suffered from psoriasis and decided to see if the water would alleviate the symptoms of the skin disease, which it did. In a newspaper interview, Valur called the place "the blue lagoon", and the name caught on at once. Soon after these trials, development of the lagoon began, with facilities at first intended primarily for people with difficult skin conditions. Towards the end of the 1990s, the area was fenced off and changing rooms were opened. Since then devel-

opment has continued, and now an extensive spa, with hotel and restaurant, is run at the lagoon. In 1999 a new bathing area was created, further away from the power plant itself. The reason why the Blue Lagoon's water has proved so effective for skin conditions is not completely clear. However, it most likely involves a combination of dissolved minerals in the geothermal fluid and the biota of the lagoon. The Blue Lagoon's biota is not very varied, and two organisms dominate. On the one hand, there is a particular species of blue-green algae, and on the other a species of bacteria that is found nowhere except the Blue Lagoon. These organisms thrive in the salty water and are thought to have a positive effect on the skin of bathers. Usually the organisms go unnoticed, but on sunny days an algal bloom sometimes occurs, and the lagoon's water take on a lovely green tinge.

Geothermal fluids in high-temperature areas like Svartsengi are usually rich in dissolved solids. Deep in the Earth, the very hot fluid in the geothermal system easily dissolves various elements and compounds in the rock that the water passes through, and the geothermal fluid carries this dissolved material with it to the surface. Compared with other high-temperature geothermal areas, the fluid at Svartsengi is unusually rich in dissolved material. The reason for this is that the source of the geothermal water at Svartsengi, deep beneath the Reykjanes peninsula, is much saltier than is common in other parts of Iceland. This is because of the influence of the ocean surrounding the peninsula. Sea enters the rock formations below the peninsula, so the groundwater at depth is salty. In this situation, it is referred to as brine, and it is usually found when holes are drilled in the ground close to the coast of Iceland. On top of the brine floats a thin layer of freshwater, originating from the rain that falls on the Reykjanes penin-

sula. To reach the brine, you first have to pass through the fresh groundwater, and at Svartsengi it is about 100-150 m down to the brine. Most of the boreholes in the area are much deeper than that, and the current production holes are between 400 and 900 m deep. The shallowest holes give only steam, but holes that are deeper than 1000 m are known as two-phase boreholes, meaning that they supply both steam and hot brine. The water surface of the geothermal reservoir therefore lies at a depth of about 700-900 m, and it has fallen appreciably since the power plant was commissioned.

The mineral-rich liquid explains the large quantity of silica-sludge that can be found on the bottom of the Blue Lagoon, and which is used in skin products from the lagoon. As mentioned before, the brine and steam supplying the power plant at Svartsengi are taken at depths of 400-900 m, and the geothermal fluid is about 230-240°C at that depth. Geothermal fluid as hot as this can contain a lot of dissolved material, and the Svartsengi brine contains mainly chloride and sodium, which combine to make sea salt, as well as calcium, potassium and silica. Other elements and ions, such as sul-

phur, carbonate and magnesium are present in much smaller quantities. On its way through the power plant, the fluid cools down, and when the discharge water is pumped out of the plant it is only 70-80 °C. When it cools, the brine is less able to hold these materials in solution. For most of the materials this is not a problem, but the silica becomes what is called "super-saturated". That means that there is too much silica in the fluid for it to remain in solution when the brine has cooled, so the silica begins to precipitate out and forms tiny opaque crystals in the water. Due to the high pressure in the pipes of the power plant, the silica does not precipitate out until the water is outside the power station, in the Blue Lagoon. Suspended silica particles also give the water its characteristic cloudy blue colour, from which the lagoon gets its name, because the silica molecules reflect best the blue portion of sunlight.

Although most people consider the Blue Lagoon a success, and it could be considered a good use of discharge water from Svartsengi, it does however encapsulate an important problem connected to geothermal power plants. Some say that the Blue Lagoon is an environmental disaster, in which discharge water from the power plant has been poured into the environment. In the Blue Lagoon's case it is perhaps taking things too far to talk about a disaster, and the Blue Lagoon is not the only lake produced by pumping discharge water from an Icelandic high-temperature power plant into the environment. Similar lakes can be seen at power plants at Bjarnarflag, Krafla and further out on Reykjanes; and the discharge water from the Nesjavellir power plant is also poured into the environment to a large extent. Discharge water from geothermal power plants contains various undesirable, and even dangerous chemicals that can, at worst, contaminate ground water over a large area below the power plant.

The discharge water in the Blue Lagoon is not the only consequence of the Svartsengi power plant either. Emissions from the geothermal power plant contain various chemical compounds, and hydrogen sulphide is one of them. Hydrogen sulphide provides the characteristic sulphurous smell of the high-temperature geothermal areas, but in high concentrations it is poisonous for the environment. Coverings of moss on the lava around the power plant show signs of having been damaged in the 40 years that have passed since Svartsengi was commissioned, and this is worrying because moss grows very slowly.

Krýsuvík

Krýsuvík is a name that is usually applied to the area southwest of Lake Kleifarvatn where, among other features, the hot spring area of Seltún and the Grænavatn explosion crater can be found. To be precise, the Krýsuvík name probably originally referred to an old inlet which cut into the south coast of the Reykjanes peninsula a little west of Kleifarvatn but. That inlet was filled by lava when the Ögmundarhraun lava was produced in the 12th century. This lava flow destroyed the first Krýsuvík farmstead, which probably stood on the eastern side of the inlet at the place now called Húshólmi, in the middle of the lava expanse. For centuries after that, the Krýsuvík farmstead stood below Bæjarfell, where old routes met, and the place name has been transferred to the area around the farm, even though it is far from the sea. Krýsuvík was an important farm for centuries, but the settlement was thought remote, and it fell into decline after about 1900.

Although the local history is complicated, Krýsuvík is no less remarkable in respect in respect to the local geology. The area is part of a volcanic system named after Krýsuvík or Trölladyngja, and this system has erupted frequently since the end of the last glaciation. The most powerful surface expression of geothermal energy in the Krýsuvík system is at Seltún – a very beautiful and colourful hot-spring area southwest of Kleifarvatn, known to most people as the Krýsuvík geothermal area. Sulphur was mined there, on and off, from at least the 18th century until the end of the 19th, and signs of the mine workings can still be seen. West of Seltún and Kleifarvatn is Sveifluháls, a long móberg (hyaloclastite) ridge that formed during subglacial eruptions in the Ice Age. Postglacial volcanic activity in the Krýsuvík system has almost all been confined to an elongate eruptive fissure west of Sveifluháls, and the volcanically active area stretches a long way north towards the capital city area. The last eruption in the Krýsuvík system lasted from 1151 to 1188, and it has been called the "Krýsuvík Fires". The previously mentioned Ögmundarhraun lava flowed then, southwards from a long crater row west of Sveifluháls, and in the north of the system the Kapelluhraun lava flowed down to the sea at Straumsvík.

The main eruptive fissure in the Krýsu-

vík system lies west of Sveifluháls, so there are few signs of volcanic activity in Krýsuvík itself even though geothermal activity is greatest there. Small lobes of lava lie north of Bæjarfell and on the eastern slopes of Sveifluháls, in addition to a strip of lava by Lake Grænavatn. The lake is one of a number of explosion craters in the Krýsuvík area that were formed in volcanic events in the last thousand years. Grænavatn is about 300 m in diameter and around 45 m deep, possibly created in two separate explosive eruptions, with the western part of lake being older than the eastern part. In the eruptions, fragments of bedrock, lava bombs and pumiceous scoria rained over the crater area, and in the lava at Grænavatn it is possible to see xenoliths, fragments of gabbro carried by the magma from deep within the Earth. The green colour of the water is due to the sulphur compounds in it. The water level marks the height of the natural water table in the area.

Although there is little volcanic activity in Krýsuvík, it is obviously a geologically active area. Early in 2009 the land surface around Krýsuvík began to rise, continuing for a few months before sinking again. In April 2010 uplift began once more and lasted for about 20 months before the land sank again. Of course, geologists were curious about this activity, and two main explanations of the uplift were put forward – that either magma had pushed its way upwards, or that gas emission had caused the uplift. Subsequent research has not shown any magma below the area, and there is no indication that an eruption is to be expected. It is most likely that gas emission, or boiling fluid in the geothermal system is the culprit.

The Krýsuvík area has long been thought suitable for harnessing geothermal energy, and exploratory drilling began there in the 1940s. Little was gained from the first boreholes and the programme continued over the next decades, but energy extraction from the area has not gone further than the exploration phase. Research shows that a broad region of high resistivity underlies the Krýsuvík region, and such areas are characteristic of active high-temperature fields and indicate high-temperature geothermal alteration of the rock. However, temperatures in research holes across the area indicate that the temperature is much lower than might be expected from the magnitude of the resistivity. This suggests that the high resistivity is more an indication of the previous temperature of the geothermal system, rather than the present situation, and that the system is cooling. Geologist Sigmundur Einarsson has written articles about the Krýsuvík area in recent years and presented a fairly compelling argument for the geothermal area being less extensive than previously thought, and that it is actually composed of several minor geothermal areas that are unable to meet the production demands required for many people.

To access the scattered pockets of energy in the Krýsuvík system would require separate constructions for all the main geothermal centres in the area, and the appearance of this sensitive area would be radically changed by such projects. In 1949 geologist Sigurður Þórarinsson spoke about nature conservation at the 60th anniversary meeting of the Icelandic Natural History Society. The poor stewardship of Grænavatn, near Krýsuvík, had driven him to protest. It would show appropriate respect for Sigurður Þórarinsson's contribution to Icelandic nature conservation if the outstanding area around Krýsuvík were declared a protected area as soon as possible, as a basis for a volcanic national park on the Reykjanes peninsula, thereby offering support for Krýsuvík and its surroundings in the future.

Þríhnúkagígur

On the outskirts of the Greater Reykjavík area, just east of the Grafarholt neighborhood, stand three separate peaks on the edge of the Bláfjöll mountain region. There, under the surface, hides one of Iceland's most unusual geological features. Together, the three peaks are called Þríhnúkar, and the westernmost one is a móberg (hyaloclastite) ridge that formed under an Ice Age glacier. The other two are lava craters that formed after the end of the last glaciation. Below the easternmost and youngest peak lies an enormous drained lava-conduit, which usually goes by the name of Þríhnúkagígur.

For a long time Þríhnúkagígur was completely unknown; it was probably discovered in the early 20th century. Its full extent and size were, however, not known until later in the century – exploring the vast space was not easy. Ophthalmologist Árni B. Stefánsson is thought to have been first to abseil into Þríhnúkugígur in 1974, and since then he has been in the vanguard of speleologists when it comes to the exploration of the crater's conduit and the presentation of it to the outside world. In 1992 Árni wrote an article for an Icelandic natural history magazine and described in detail the cave below the crater and its environment. This was the first complete description of the crater's conduit. Since then, some interesting research has been done on the area, particularly in connection with plans to open the cave to the public.

The Þríhnúkar peaks are surrounded by a vast lava field which resulted from a number of eruptions west of the Bláfjöll mountains after the end of glaciation. The Bláfjöll mountains are móberg (hyaloclastite) mountains that formed in eruptions beneath Ice Age glaciers. The area belongs to the Brennisteinsfjöll volcanic system, which

is slightly to the south, on the Reykjanes peninsula, and from the volcanic landscape and volume of lava it can be seen that this volcanic system is very active. As mentioned before, the westernmost of the three peaks is made of móberg, and formed beneath a glacier. The two younger craters, on the other hand, are quite recent; both were formed earlier than about 3500–5000 years ago, as determined by ash layers, and there is probably about 1000 years age difference between them. There have been eruptions in the area since the three peaks were formed – the Húsfellsbruni lava fields, for example, these lava fields were created during Iceland's settlement period.

Þríhnúkagígur is an enormous cavern beneath the easternmost peak – the eruption conduit of the volcano that formed the peak and the lava lobes east and west of it. The peak stands about 30–40 m higher than the surrounding land, and the entrance to the crater is at about 550 m above sea level. From the entrance it is, however, about a 120 m deep vertical fall down to the bottom of the crater conduit, deep below the surface of the land surrounding the Þríhnúkar peaks. The crater conduit is even deeper off to the side, and the southwest branch of the cavern is deepest – almost 200 m lower than the entrance. The cavern is not just deep; it is also wide. The conduit mouth is not very wide, about four metres in diameter, but it broadens rapidly, and at a depth of about 60 m it opens into an enormous cavern that is about as high as the tower of Reykjavík's largest church, Hallgrímskirkja. At this depth, the eruption conduit is very elongate, almost three times longer than it is wide. This reflects the fissure-like eruption channel – it originally erupted along a short eruptive fissure. The volume of Þríhnúkagígur is about 150,000 m³, similar to Iceland's largest indoor football stadium, and it is among the deepest and biggest lava caverns known on Earth.

The crater conduit began to form at the very start of the volcanic eruption that created the crater. In the events leading up to the eruption, magma slowly and steadily moved its way up from a great depth in the crust, along fractures in the bedrock. When the magma had reached a relatively shallow depth, perhaps a few hundred metres below the surface, an eruption was unavoidable. At that point in time, gas in the magma was increasingly forming bubbles due to the reduction in pressure, and the rapid expansion of the gas propelled the magma upwards. It eventually spluttered out of the eruptive fissure at the surface. The eruption in Þríhnúkagígur was fairly small and hardly lasted long, but while it did, the magma flowed steadily up the elongate eruption channel. As the eruption proceeded, the eruption channel became narrower, as can be seen by the solidified coating of lava inside the upper part of the channel. And as the eruption's power dwindled, the main flow of magma became concentrated in one crater while the eruption shut down gradually in the others. This can be seen in a large, closed eruption channel leading up from the cavern to the side of the crater opening, and also in a long, narrow, vertical eruption channel at about 180 m deep in the southwest-section of the cavern. This eruption channel is believed to have fed some smaller craters southwest of Þríhnúkagígur, and may have closed fairly early in the eruption.

At the end of the Þríhnúkagígur eruption, most of the action in the fissure-shaped eruption channel was over. Usually, the final remnants of magma from an eruption solidify in the eruption channel and form a dyke. However, for some reason, Þríhnúkagígur's eruption channel drained at the end of the eruption, so the upper part of the channel was left empty. The original eruption channel only partially drained though, and a dyke associated with the eruption can be seen along the length of the roof in the southwest section of the cavern – the magma there had already solidified before the channel drained. Not only did the eruption channel empty, the solid rock around the crater also supported it and stopped it from collapsing completely. Rock-falls from the walls of the eruption channel have been unavoidable, and the original walls of the channel have mostly collapsed inwards at depths of over 80 m below the crater opening, creating a large heap of rock in the middle of the cave. It is this collapse of the walls that has in fact created the wide cavern, and without it the channel would be much narrower and more elongate. In this context it is worth pointing out the inaccurate vocabulary used in reports about Þríhnúkagígur – the crater conduit is frequently said to be an example of a magma chamber that emptied at the end of the eruption. Usually the concept of a magma chamber is used for a large intrusion in the heart of a central volcano, usually at a few kilometres' depth. Use of the term magma chamber here implies that the magma paused in the cavern on its way up to the surface, but this could hardly have been the case. Rather, it pushed upwards to the surface without stopping, and the present cavern was in reality only a narrow channel while the eruption was taking place.

Understandably, it is not easy to access Þríhnúkagígur, and for a long time only experienced abseilers could go down. In the summer of 2012 tourists and the general public were given the opportunity to ride in a lift down to the bottom of the crater conduit, and this experience is highly recommended. Since the turn of the last century there have been ideas about opening the crater conduit even more to the public by boring a tunnel into the cavern. The main idea is based on drilling a tunnel a few hundred metres long, which would enter the crater conduit at some height above its bottom, and a viewing platform would give people the chance to enjoy this great natural wonder. Proponents of this idea believe that Þríhnúkagígur could easily become one of the best-known destinations for foreign tourists in Iceland, and there is no reason to doubt it since the cavern is magnificent in every way. The author of this book is, however, far from convinced that it is right to open the cave to more visitors. The project appears achievable, but that does not mean that it has to be realised. Easy access would give many people the opportunity to visit the cave, but at the same time the experience would be completely changed, especially in view of plans for several hundred thousands visitors there every year. In the narrow confines of the cave, it is not at all certain that the experience of each member of the crowd would be anything like the effect that the crater now has on a guest.

Those who champion the plan have pointed out that the project is mostly reversible; it would be simple to remove the viewing platform and close the tunnel. In the case of Þríhnúkagígur, it would be very expensive to open, and although at a later date there might be reason to prevent access to the cave, because of severe disturbance or damage for example, it is not certain that the interests of nature will weigh heavily enough against financial gain. By then the environment will already have been disturbed, and the pristine surroundings of Þríhnúkar would largely be lost. There is every reason to tread cautiously and ask whether a natural phenomenon is being forced into a type of tourism where it may not belong. A big part of the adventure of going down Þríhnúkagígur is the difficult access to it. Would "assembly line tourism" perhaps mean the death of the crater and the thrill that it gives its guests?

Grábrók

Grábrók is a beautiful scoria crater close to the main road in the Norðurárdalur valley, just north of Bifröst. It was formed in a medium-sized volcanic eruption about 3200 years ago. Grábrók and its neighbouring craters are the only volcanoes that erupted in Norðurárdalur after the end of glaciation. For this reason, the Grábrókarhraun lava field has a special status in western Borgarfjörður. It is odd to travel around the vegetated bog land and grey, glaciated basalt crags in Borgarfjörður and have the rough, moss-green Grábrókarhraun suddenly rear its head. Grábrók has been a protected natural feature since 1962, and the craters and lava create a very beautiful landscape in the Borgarfjörður area.

Grábrók is part of the active Snæfellsnes Volcanic Belt that reaches from Snæfellsjökull west to Grábrók, which is on the eastern end of the volcanic belt. Grábrók had long been considered to be about 3600–4000 years old, but in 2006 the lava was carbon dated when the Grábrókarhraun lava was being drilled into during groundwater research. When the lava was drilled through, small birch twigs were carried up with the rock samples; the lava had flowed over them when it was erupted. They proved to be about 3200 years old, and that defines the age of the lava. The eruption was probably along a relatively short eruptive fissure at first, perhaps 600–800 m long, but most activity was very soon concentrated in three separate craters. They are called Grábrók, Grábrókarfell and Litla-Grábrók, and the first two are considerably larger than Litla-Grábrók, which is almost totally overshadowed by its siblings. Litla-Grábrók was actually nibbled at before the area was protected, and material from it was used as road aggregate. By about 1960 the effects

of quarrying were becoming quite obvious, and people decided to have the area protected, and managed to save Litla-Grábrók to a large extent, even though part of it has gone.

In the old days, people hiked up Grábrók from many directions, and old tracks are scattered over the mountain like scars, but now a clearly marked trail goes from a car park, up the north side of the mountain. The path travels over vegetated lava, and birch dominates, woolly fringe-moss coats the surface of the lava and the brick-red scoria of the crater. Just above the steps by the car park, you can see an interesting feature which tells us a lot about the inner formation of a scoria cone like Grábrók. In the middle of the path the upper half of a small lava channel can be glimpsed, looking a lot like a half-buried sewage pipe. Lava has flowed through this lava channel, coming underground from the Grábrók crater, and no doubt there are many similar small lava channels on the outside of Grábrók, buried by lava and scoria. If the path is followed upwards it soon splits in three, one path goes up to the crater, and another continues down Grábrók and over to Grábrókarfell. Where the path divides, two larger lava channels can be seen. One of them is above the path, on the right-hand side of the steps which lead up to the crater itself, and this channel is about a metre or more wide. Below the path, there is a drystone pen built in Grábrók's main lava channel. The channel opens about 50 m above the pen, and below that point it forms a pretty big lava tunnel down which the stream of lava from Grábrók flowed. Based on the altitude difference between the lava tunnel and the crater, it is clear that the lava stream from the crater lay at quite a depth relative to the current surface.

In the crater itself there are many interesting things to see. If you follow the path up to the crater rim you can see how splashes of lava have flattened out on top of each other and built up the crater walls. Another thing worth noticing is that approximately in the middle of Grábrók is another smaller crater, with low walls that just skim the bottom of the main crater. Central craters like this are a sign of dwindling power towards the end of the eruption, and they can be found widely in craters, including what are called rootless craters.. The eruption's power fades little by little, and in its final phase a small mini-crater builds up around the vent. Such a crater is also present in Grábrókarfell, and it can be seen in the aerial photograph on the Environmental Agency's sign by the car park.

Grábrók is an unusual phenomenon with an exceptionally beautiful round shape. This shape is common in scoria cones in the Snæfellsnes Volcanic Belt, and Grábrók declares its family connection to volcanoes such as Búðaklettur, Rauðamelskúla and Saxhóll. Grábrók is also one of the few craters occurring next to the main road, and it is hardly possible to find a volcano with better access than the Grábrók crater. Passers-by should stop and enjoy this amazing geological site.

Hraunfossar and Barnafoss

Hraunfossar is the name of some beautiful small waterfalls that emit from beneath the Hallmundarhraun lava, out into the river Hvítá. The water in the falls is crystal-clear spring water, and Hvíta contains glacial meltwater, so the contrast between the waterfalls and the river is tremendous. Upstream from Hraunfossar are many small falls or rapids in the river Hvítá, and they are collectively called Barnafoss. There, Hvítá flows off the edge of the lava field, and it has slowly eroded down into the friable edge of the lava and formed many tiny gullies. For years there have been stone arches across the river at Barnafoss; they are formed by the erosion of the river in the porous lava. Erosion is greatest in major floods; Hvítá escapes its banks then, and there are clear signs of this at Barnafoss.

In the early 10th century there was a big eruption in craters at the edge of the Langjökull icecap. The Hallmundarhraun lava flowed from these craters - Borgarfjörður's largest postglacial lava. The eruption was probably a long one, maybe lasting a few years, and. The lava flowed about 50 km westwards from the crater, north of Eiríksjökull and Strútur, and all the way to Hvítá's current river course at Hraunfossar. It is impossible to tell where Hvítá's course was before the lava erupted, but the river probably sought out the nook along the lava's edge soon after it was erupted. Upstream

from Hraunfossar, the Hallmundarhraun lava is rough and difficult to traverse, but at the same time it is porous and friable. So Hvítá could easily dig its way into the lava at Barnafoss.

Erosion by large rivers such as Hvítá is greatest when the rivers are in flood. During flooding, the river carries more sediment, and it also flows faster than it usually does. With the extra speed of the water, the river can carry along larger stones, which roll or bounce along the river bottom and erode it. Where the river meets resistance, a long-term eddy forms, and the river often excavates circular potholes in its bed. If the river succeeds in digging down and under the rock, stone arches form. There have no doubt been many stone arches over the years at Barnafoss, but because of the river's erosion most of them eventually collapse. There is one stone arch just below Barnafoss, but it is not at all safe to cross.

The Hraunfossar waterfalls appear where groundwater streams from beneath the lava. Because Hallmundarhraun is a recent, unaltered lava all the water that falls on it trickles down through the lava, so there are no rivers on its surface. Below the permeable lava, however, lie older, less permeable rocks, and they are not as porous as the lava. So precipitation that falls on Hallmundarhraun flows at a relatively shal-

low depth below the lava, on impermeable layers of rock. Where the Hvítá river flows along the edge of the Hallmundarhraun lava below Barnafoss, it has eroded below the level of the lava into the underlying impermeable rock. This is why the groundwater streams out from under the lava, over a long stretch, falling into the Hvítá river as the Hraunfossar waterfalls. Although the waterfalls are unique, it must be presumed that the groundwater flow is just as high elsewhere. However, because of the aforementioned situation, the waterfalls only appear at Hraunfossar. In many other places in Iceland similar waterfalls can be seen, where groundwater emits from beneath porous lava fields.

From the viewing platform by Hvítá there is a good view across Hraunfossar, and it is possible to see both how the water comes from beneath the lava, and the impermeable clay layer that the waterfalls flow off it. Hvítá carries about twenty times the volume of water in the Hraunfossar falls, but most of the river water runs in a deep channel close to the far bank, and the river sometimes appears to have less water than it actually does. A little higher up the river, Barnafoss is reached, where a stone arch can be seen down by the water surface. Special attention is drawn to the fact that the arch is impassable, and fatal accidents have happened in the river here, so great care must be taken. If the canyon is examined closer, it can be seen that the lava flowed in a few different layers and created a thick stack of lava flows – they all came from the same eruption.

It is perfect to cross the Hvítá river on the footbridge below Barnafoss. From the bridge it is easy to see how the Hvítá flows in one deep, main channel, and also how the river flows along the edge of Hallmundarhraun, as there is no lava on the side of the river where the viewing platform is. On the far side of the river you can see a strange feature on the riverbank just below Barnafoss. A light-brown dyke twists along the middle of the lava, contrasting oddly with the dark surroundings. Regardless of the beauty of the nearby waterfalls, the dyke is just as remarkable. A dyke like this one forms underground, as a magma conduit in a volcano. In other words, the dyke tells us about the older geological history of the area. In the highest part of Borgarfjörður, inland from Hraunfossar and Barnafoss, there used to be a large central volcano. The central volcano is usually referred as after Húsafell, and it was active about 2-3 million years ago. Signs of the Húsafell central volcano can still be seen widely in the area, at the stunningly beautiful Selgil for example, just east of the old Húsafell farm. The light-coloured dyke at Barnafoss is also part of the volcano, and its light colour indicates that the dyke is made of rhyolite.

You could say that the old and the new meet at Hraunfossar - remnants of the old Húsafell volcano lie beneath the "brand new" Hallmundarhraun. About two million years separate the formation of these two features, which is quite a long time in Icelandic geological history. Such a situation is not unique in the geology of Iceland, and is common in other countries as well. Where this happens, geologists talk about an unconformity. An unconformity means that the rock layers do not sit one on top of the other in an uninterrupted pile; instead there is a layer or more missing. The layers that are missing have been removed in some way, by glacial erosion for example, and it is often a headache for geologists to try and work out what has happened. There are not many places where it is easy for the inexperienced to see an unconformity in the rocks, but the area below Barnafoss is exceptionally good for this.

Eldborg in Hnappadalur

Volcanic activity in Iceland is concentrated in certain geographical areas called volcanic belts. The majority of activity occurs in the rift zones that lie across the country from southwest to northeast, along the tectonic plate boundaries. However, some patches of Icelandic postglacial volcanism are not connected to these rift zones, at least not in an obvious way. Among them is the volcanic belt on the Snæfellsnes peninsula, reaching all the way from the vast Snæfellsjökull volcano, along the length of the peninsula to Grábrók, its easternmost point. Volcanic activity can be seen widely on the peninsula, and one of its characteristics is that most of the eruptions took place on very short fissures, unlike the long fissure eruptions in the rift zone. This can be attributed to there be-

ing no extensional rifting on Snæfellsnes, so no big fissure eruptions happen there.

Part of the Snæfellsnes Volcanic Belt lies through the Hnappadalur valley, on the southern side of the peninsula, and it is interesting to walk around the valley and look at the great selection of volcanoes on offer there. Eldborg, close to the valley mouth, is undoubtedly the best known of them – a very beautifully shaped crater that can be seen from many places on the peninsula. Its rim rises 50 m above the Elborgarhraun lava, and the crater is about 50 m deep. From a distance Eldborg appears almost perfectly circular, but it is actually slightly oval, about 250 m long and 180 m wide. Many people think that Eldborg is a lone crater, but when examined carefully it is clear that the erup-

tion was along a very short fissure. In total, five craters can be made out, although Eldborg is by far the largest of them. For a long time it was believed that Eldborgarhraun was erupted after Iceland's settlement period. This was based on an account in Landnámabók, the Book of Settlements, where it tells of pioneer Sel-Þór Grímsson who colonised and lived at Ýtri-Rauðamel in Hnappadalur. In the Book of Settlements it says:

"Þórir was old and blind when he came outside late in the evening and saw a big and aggressive man row into the Kaldárós estuary in a war-ship, walk up to the farm that was at Hrípur, and dig by the gate of the sheep pen; in the night an eruption started there, and Borgarhraun burned. The farm was where the crater now stands."

This obviously refers to Eldborg, and some people have thought that this was a description of the volcano's formation late in the settlement period. Generally speaking however, geologists have considered that all the lava in Hnappadalur had been erupted long before the settlement period. In 1955 an Icelandic geologist put forward the theory that the Eldborg lava actually flowed in two eruptions. First a smooth pahoehoe lava that makes up most of the Eldborgarhraun lava field was erupted, but around the crater itself is rough 'a'a lava. The geologist thought that various differences between these lavas pointed to different ages, and it was not unlikely that the 'a'a lava was erupted after the settlement period. In 1978, however, geologist Haukur Jóhannesson advanced a convincing argument for Eldborgarhraun having flowed in a single eruption about 5000–9000 years ago. The difference in appearance simply indicates different phases in the eruption, whereby the pahoehoe lava formed first and the rough aa lava later. The formation of Eldborg itself occurred when, towards the end of the eruption, all the activity

became concentrated in one crater which grew over the other craters on the fissure. At that point in time the lava was thin-flowing, and filled the main crater with a lava lake that alternately rose and fell within the crater rim. At its highest level the lava lake left layers of semi-solidified lava on the rim of the crater, building it higher.

Haukur not only demonstrated the older age of Eldborg in his article, he also directed readers' attention towards another volcano in Hnappadalur, at Rauðhálsar. It sits furthest east in the valley, below the mountain Kolbeinsstaðafjall, and a fairly large lava stream flowed from it towards the west. Haukur excavated soil profiles at several places in the southern part of Hnappadalur to study the layers of volcanic ash from the Rauðhálsar volcano. In most of the profiles there was a clear colour difference in the soil where black peat changes to brown peat; this colour change has been traced to the influence of human activities after the settlement period. Almost everywhere, the ash layer from Rauðhálsar is found at this colour change, or just above it. This lends weight to the tale in the Book of Settlements, which might after all hold some grain of truth. The story has, however, shifted from Rauðhálsar to Eldborg, which is perhaps understandable in the light of the crater's dignified presence.

A hiking path leads from the main road by Snorrastaðir, to Eldborg. The route goes through the shrub-covered hillocks and dells of Eldborgarhraun, all the way to the crater row. There, the path threads across the smaller craters, Rauðhóll, Litla-Eldborg and Öxl, before continuing up Eldborg itself. There is a good opportunity to look at the construction of the crater rim and see how the crater is mostly built from thin, red-coloured layers of lava.

Búðahraun

Búðahraun, on the south side of the Snæfellsnes peninsula, is one of the many beautiful lava fields scattered around the peninsula. It is not very showy, but it makes an attractive background for Búðir and the beach. In the middle of the lava is a rounded crater called Búðaklettur, and the lava flowed from this in a single eruption a few thousand years ago. Búðahraun was given protected status in 1977, and it is known for its unusually varied plant life. Eleven of the sixteen species of fern found in Iceland can be seen there, and over 130 species of higher plants have been identified growing on the lava. The lava field and its surroundings are also closely connected with the history of Snæfellsnes and Borgarfjörður, and old signs of human habitation can be found in most parts of the lava.

The Búðahraun lava was formed in an eruption long before Iceland was settled, as indeed were all the lavas on the peninsula apart from Rauðhálsahraun in Hnappadalur. A little east of Búðaklettur are signs of a small crater fragment that is either the remnant of another crater on the original eruptive fissure, or a rootless crater formed when the lava flowed into bog or the sea. As the lava field stands next to the coast, it is reasonable to assume that it flowed into the sea when it was erupted, but there are few signs of the explosive activity that accompanies the meeting of lava and water. Geologists therefore think it likely that the lava was erupted when the sea level around Iceland was lower than it is now. That was the case about 5000–8000 years ago, and at that time the sea level was up to dozens of metres lower than it is now. So it is likely that Búðahraun dates from then.

The lava is known for its great natural beauty, and its great variety of plant life, but its geology is no less interesting. The lava is quite rough in many places and difficult to traverse. Here and there, deep holes and crevasses can be seen, but also beautiful and vegetated dells. The sea even invades the deepest holes at high tide, because the bottom of the lava lies below sea level. But the geology first becomes fascinating when the inner make-up of the lava is examined. If bits of the Búðahraun lava are examined, then one of its main characteristics can be seen. Small crystals of different colours can be seen in the lava mass at many localities, and such crystals are called phenocrysts. Búðahraun is said to be a porphyritic lava because it contains phenocrysts, and porphyritic lavas are very common in Iceland. What makes Búðahraun special is that it has three different sorts of phenocrysts, while most porphyritic lavas in Iceland have only one or two. In the Búðahraun lava it is possible to see white phenocrysts of the mineral plagiclase, green phenocrysts of olivine, and black ones of pyroxene. Phenocrysts like these form over quite a long period, in the magma at some depth, before it breaks its way to the surface in an eruption. It could be said that the crystals are older than the mass of the lava that encases them – the lava mass is made of much smaller crystals. But please note that the lava is protected by law, so breaking off pieces of lava or taking any away is forbidden. Although the lava field looks enormous and there seems to be plenty to spare, all damage – even when it seems very minor – can quickly result in major scarring. So it is best to enjoy the lava and the natural beauty on the spot.

It is popular to travel on foot or horseback across the lava, and then the old routes are taken. First you follow the coastline at Búðir – the beach there is thought to be very unusual. There are a lot of green sand grains on the beach, and they come from the olivine crystals in the Búðahraun lava, which the sea has broken down over time. From Búðakirkja it is perfect to hike to Frambúðir, where it is thought a fishing community stood in the early years of the settlement period. Frambúðir was the original "Búðir" after which the lava field and locality are named, but the community moved to the current position after Básendaflóð, a very destructive sea-flood in 1799. From Frambúðir the path twists along the old Klettsgata route in the middle of the lava field, over to Miðhús, clearly marked in the rocks by the traffic of past centuries. The route itself is an easy one, and obvious to any who wish to go to Búðaklettur or some of the lava caves that can be found nearby, particularly in the lava on the western side. Best known of them is Búðahellir, a cave which has long been famous and is well known from folk history. Búðahellir was thought to be incredibly long, and this was confirmed when it was measured in 1975 it was measured and mapped. It is 382 m long, with nine openings, and one end is in the Búðaklettur crater itself.

Snæfellsjökull

In 1864, Snæfellsjökull shot to fame when the renowned science fiction author Jules Verne published his book, *Journey to the Centre of the Earth (Voyage au centre de la Terre)*. In the book, the main protagonist, Professor Otto Lidenbrock, sails to Iceland where he enters the crater of the Snæfellsjökull volcano along with his travel companions, on the way to the strangest of adventures. The novel first came out in Icelandic in 1944 under the title *Leyndardómar Snæfellsjökuls: för í iður jarðar*. This is often shortened to *Leyndardómar Snæfellsjökuls*, so Jules Verne's novel is best known in Icelandic as *Secrets of Snæfellsjökull,* even though this does not quite match the title in its original language. The interesting thing about the Icelandic title is that it would be just as suitable for an article about the geology of Snæfellsjökull. Though it is pretty certain that neither a huge subterranean ocean nor dinosaurs are to be found in the bowels of Snæfellsjökull, there is a great deal that scientists do not know about its geology, despite considerable research in recent decades. Since Snæfellsjökull is a big, active volcano, priority should be given to improving knowledge of the area in the next few years.

The Snæfellsjökull volcano has the classical cone shape of a stratovolcano, and is readily visible from many locations across western Iceland. It is a central volcano which has erupted regularly through geological history, and it is by far the most active central volcano in the Snæfellsnes volcanic belt. The entire rim of the Snæfellsnes peninsula west of Búðir, belongs to the Snæfellsjökull volcanic system, which is the most active on Snæfellsnes. The oldest layers of lava in the roots of Snæfellsjökull

have been dated, and they are thought to be about 840,000 years old. The mountain has therefore built up over a long time, and there is a great variety of rock types and volcanic features in and around Snæfellsjökull. Since the Ice Age glacier vanished from Iceland around 10,000 years ago, three large eruptions of Snæfellsjökull have occurred. The last eruption in the summit crater of Snæfellsjökull happened about 1800 years ago, and it was probably the largest eruption since the end of regional glaciation. The eruption began as a powerful explosive eruption, and a sizable layer of acid ash and pumice is attributed to it. Due to the explosive activity, part of the glacier melted and considerable floods of water flowed down the northwest side of the mountain. This initial phase of the eruption did not last long, and then lava started to flow down the volcano's sides, to the north and south. These lava flows are prominent where they snake down the sides of the volcano, particularly on the southern side. It is not unlikely that the highest peaks at the top of Snæfellsjökull, called Þúfur, were formed in this eruption.

Preceding this eruption, there were large eruptions about 4000 and 7000-9000 years ago. Between all these large eruptions there were many minor eruptions on the flanks of the stratovolcano and on the lowlands west and south of the glacier. The whole of the tip of the Snæfellsjökull peninsula bears glorious testimony to the activity in the Snæfellsnes volcanic system, and most of the peninsula is covered by a variety of lava fields, both smooth pahoehoe lavas and rougher aa lavas. Many beautiful volcanoes are scattered across the peninsula. Among them are Hólahólar, Öndverðarneshólar and the two at Saxhólar – although the more southern of these is badly scarred by an old gravel quarry. It is popular to drive over the lava field at

Öndverðarnes, and many people walk along the south coast. Unusual jointed, columnar formations can be seen in many places, particularly at Hellnar and Arnarstapi. A little west of Hellnar are pillars of rock, called Lóndrangar. They are old volcanic plugs, the remains of volcanoes that erupted on the coastline at the end of the regional glaciation, and which were then mostly eroded away by the ocean. More recent lavas have flowed between the plugs and the land, and connected them to the mainland again.

The youngest lava in the Snæfellsjökull system is named Væjuhraun (sometimes called Væruhraun), and it lies on top of an ash layer from Snæfellsjökull's last major eruption. So it is somewhat less than 1800 years old; since it was erupted, the Snæfellsnes system has been dormant. Although it has been a long time since the volcano last erupted, it is only a matter of time before it makes its presence known once more. It could happen in our time, or just as likely after a hundred or a thousand years. It is therefore important to keep an eye on the area and install a monitoring system on the peninsula, even though there is no real reason to fear a sudden eruption because eruptions in stratovolcanoes of this size would probably be preceded by substantial signs. Although an eruption is hardly imminent, there have been other rapid changes to the mountain. Since about 1900 the surface area of the glacier has halved, and the volume of ice has shrunk by about two-thirds. Sadly, the outlook is that the Snæfellsjökull icecap will vanished within a few decades. The mountain will certainly still be there – will it be strange to call it Snæfellsjökull when there is no "jökull" left?

Rauðasandur

Rauðasandur is a roughly 12-13 km long beach on the south coast of the West Fjords, just east of Látrabjarg. It has often been said that the beach and its surroundings are one of Iceland's most beautiful natural features, and the region has long been renowned for its landscape and flourishing farms. Rauðasandur is one of the largest shell-sand beaches in Iceland, the sand getting its red tinge from fragments of scallop shells. The area is enclosed by mountains, and the beach ends in cliffs and steep screes, both east and west of the sands. To the west lies Brekkuhlíð, and further away, on the far side of Keflavík, is Látrabjarg. To the east is Skorarfjall and its scree slopes. At the end of the last glaciation, just after the glaciers left this area, the sea level was higher and the surrounding mountains stood on the coast. Signs of a higher sea level can be widely seen, where sea-worn rocks lie much higher than the current sea level. After the land rose, shallows were formed, and time and tide have filled the beach with the red-coloured sand. The shells break under the force of the waves, which pulverise them in the shallow water offshore. Various species of fish also grind the shells and then deposit them again. Rauðasandur is a beautiful example of the formation of a sandy beach – if an aerial photograph of the beach is studied, it shows how the ocean waves carry the sand back and forth, from the eastern part beach and out towards Látrabjarg.

But why is the Rauðasandur beach so rich in shells, and especially scallop shells? Obviously the answer is that there are a lot of shells in the Breiðafjörður bay. The bay has always been a treasure house of food, and good fishing grounds can be found there, including areas of scallops. Breiðafjörður was actually Iceland's most prolific fishing ground for scallops by far, while the scallop was being fished. Around 80% or more of the country's total catch was fished in the bay, but the main habitat and fishing area for the scallop is in the southern part of the bay, between Stykkishólmur and Flatey. So it seems a little odd that most of the shells are found in the northwest of the bay. Shell beaches are few or non-existent east of Vatnsfjörður, and in the south of Breiðafjörður the shell beaches are much smaller than those of Rauðasandur.

The reason why Rauðasandur has a much greater volume of scallop shells than any other beach in Breiðafjörður is the orientation of marine currents in the

bay. Breiðafjörður is known for big and strong currents, and they are at their heaviest furthest out in the bay, on both the north and south sides. The current system in Breiðafjörður is complicated, but a flow model of the ocean around the country has been developed which manages to mimic fairly well the ocean currents in Breiðafjörður. The model shows that from the main scallop ground north of Stykkishólmur, the current lies northwards in the bay, towards the coast west of Vatnsfjörður. From there the sea flows past Barðaströnd, Rauðasandur and Látrabjarg, around Bjargtangar and then along the north coast of the West Fjords. The model also explains the distribution of shell sands in inlets north of Bjargtangar. In Látravík, Breiðavík and Kollsvík, beautiful shell beaches can be seen – similar to Rauðasandur and the shell beaches along Barðaströnd, but more golden in colour. The colour is explained by there being less volume of scallop shells than at Rauðasandur, and more of other shells such as clams.

Látrabjarg

Látrabjarg is the westernmost point in Iceland. It has often been called the westernmost point in Europe too, although that is a matter of definition because the Azores, which belong to Portugal, lie further west. Látrabjarg is made of old, preglacial lava formations, and this part of the West Fjords was built up in repeated eruptions around 12–14 million years ago. Between the layers of lava are old soil horizons that are more readily eroded than the lavas, and these soil horizons form good shelves for nesting birds.

Látrabjarg is a sea cliff, about 14 km long, stretching from Bjargtangar in the west to Keflavík in the east. It is over 440 m high at Heiðnakinn, its highest point, and most of the cliff is about 300 m high, or more. Millions of seabirds breed and live on the cliff in summer time, and it is also said to be the largest bird cliff in Europe, even possibly in the world according to some.

From the westernmost part of the cliff at Bjargtangar, it is about a six-kilometre walk along the cliff edge east to Heiðnakinn, and most of the birds are on this route. The view from Heiðnakinn to Breiðafjörður and the nearby area is spectacular. Because of the huge number of birds in the cliff, it has always been a great source of food, and local people have abseiled down in search of both birds and eggs. Accidents have not been uncommon though, and abseiling and collecting trips on the cliff more or less stopped after a terrible accident there in 1926 when two men fell to their deaths.

Látrabjarg has not only had a place in Icelandic history as an area abundant in sources of food, seafarers have always detested it too. Strong ocean currents lie out in Breiðafjörður, past Látrabjarg, and the place where the current rounds Bjargtangar is called Látraröst (röst means whirlpool).

Good fishing grounds are on either side of Látraröst, and out beyond it, so fishermen have been going there for a long time. The area also lies on a busy sea route. However, the strong sea currents mean that even in reasonably good weather it is difficult to steer boats and ships past the cliff and around Bjargtangar. Eddies and turbulent water are formed there, far out from the land, and people avoid sailing closer to land than a few sea miles. Many shipping accidents have occurred under Látrabjarg, and there is almost nowhere along the cliff where a boat can be landed. If a boat or ship is wrecked by the cliff, the heavy seas do not take long to reduce the craft to matchwood. The last wreck at Látrabjarg was in December 1947 when the British trawler Dhoon ran aground. A remarkable rescue took place, achieved by people living at Útvíkur, which is the collective name for the three inlets north of Látrabjarg.

Látrabjarg is most accessible from Bjargtangar. From there it is easy to look at the geology of the cliff and the birds. The cliff is formed of lava of varying thicknesses, and between the lava lie old soil horizons which erode more easily than the lava layers. Shelves form on top of each layer, and the seabirds lie on their eggs there. At Bjarg-

tangar, where the cliff is lowest, there are only three or four different lava layers, but at Heiðnakinn there are 26 layers of lava. If you walk along the edge of the cliff, it is possible to view the lava layers in many places. At Ritugjá (rita means kittiwake), about 300 m from Bjargtangar, there is a large fissure in the cliff where it is convenient to view the lava layers down to sea level. Lowest in the cliff, at sea level, you can see low caves where the sea has carved out the rock. The caves extend some distance into the cliff, and when erosion by the waves has gone far enough, the overlying section of rock will collapse. As soon as the section of rock has fallen, the waves begin to break it down, and so bit by bit the cliff is gradually removed. The largest section of rock that lies beneath the cliff is called Stórurð, and it is home to almost 40% of the world's razorbill population. A little east of Ritugjá is Barði, a large dyke that juts about 60 m out from the cliff, into the sea. Barði is about 80 m high and it is thought that around 15,000 birds live there in summer.

Like other bird cliffs, Látrabjarg is loose and unstable in many places and rock falls can happen without warning. The cliff must therefore be approached with care.

Dynjandi

Dynjandi is an impressive waterfall on the river Dynjandisá, in the bottom of Arnarfjörður. The waterfall gets its name from the thundering noise that comes from it and even carries for long distances out into the fjord in good weather. Dynjandi is best seen from below, where the farm of the same name used to stand, down by the sea. From there it is possible to drive a few hundred metres off the main road (Vestfjarðavegur) to a car park by the river, and from there it is possible to walk up to the waterfall. Five other smaller waterfalls are in Dynjandisá below Dynjandi itself, and you walk past them on the way up to Dynjandi. There are a few smaller waterfalls above Dynjandi too, which are possible to look at if you walk to Dynjandi from above. The Dynjandisá river is fed by surface water, and it flows down from the vast Gláma highlands in the middle of the West Fjords.

The landscape at Dynjandisvogur is typical West Fjords landscape, if it can be put like that. The mountains surrounding the bay are made of many thick layers of lava that flowed in eruptions about 12-13 million years ago, when an active volcanic belt was located in the West Fjords. Ice Age glaciers have since dissected the land, creating deep fjords and valleys above them. Dynjandisvogur is an old cirque, a bowl-like valley which the Ice Age glacier eroded backwards into the edge of the Gláma highland where the glacier flowed down the Fremridalur valley, just north of Dynjandi. Each layer of lava in the lava pile was formed in a single eruption, and between the eruptions quite a bit of time passed. It is thought that about 5,000-12,000 years went by, on average, between lava flows in the West Fjords peninsula. So quite a lot of soil was able to form in the interval between

eruptions, and there are thin soil horizons between lavas in the pile. These soil horizons are usually red coloured and often called "red interbeds" - the red colour is due to a large amount of iron in the ancient soil. Since the red interbeds are made of old soil, they are softer than the lava layers, and they are more easily eroded than the lava layers.

The prominent terraces in the Dynjandi waterfall exist because the waterfall cascades off one layer after another, so Dynjandi is actually made up of many small waterfalls. Each lava flow in the mountainside acts as a "cap rock". A cap rock is a layer of rock which is harder than the rock underneath it. In the case of Dynjandi, it is the lava flows in the lava pile which are harder than the red interbeds between the lavas, and this creates many small waterfalls on the mountainside.

Dynjandi is not a very voluminous waterfall, and the average yearly flow in the Dynjandisá river is quite a bit less than in the Elliðaá river in Reykjavík. So it could be said that the flow is not in proportion to the magnificence of the falls in the river. During floods though, the flow can often be ten times the average rate, and the power of the river increases dramatically, as does the thundering sound of the waterfall. There are two main flood seasons in the river, as is usually the case in surface-fed rivers like Dynjandisá. Spring floods occur in May and June when the snow on the heaths melts, but it is more common to have winter floods. These are rain and meltwater floods that occur late in autumn or during the winter period.

Naustahvilft

The West Fjords are considered by some to be the most dramatic part of Iceland. The spectacular landscape and the fjords where mountains embrace those living there enchant many who go there. As mentioned in an earlier chapter of this book, the West Fjords peninsula has been dissected by Ice Age glaciers, and we can thank the Ice Age for the narrow and deep fjords. One of the most beautiful products of the glaciation is the number of cirques (corries) that can be seen in many places in the mountains of the West Fjords. One of these cirques is the immense and beautifully shaped Naustahvilft in Skutulsfjörður, facing the town of Ísafjörður. A marked hiking trail goes up to Naustahvilft, known locally as Skessusæti or She-troll's Chair, and the route is neither long nor dif-

ficult although it is quite steep underfoot. Naustahvilft is one of many cirques carved in the mountains on the south side of Skutulsfjörður, and it is both the outermost and the widest of them, as well as the lowest - its bottom lies about 220 m above sea level.

Landscape features like Naustahvilft are formed by the erosion or carving action of cirque glaciers, and although cirque glaciers have left their mark in most parts of Iceland they are particularly noticeable in the West Fjord peninsula. Well over a hundred place names in the area west of Ísafjarðardjúp are connected to cirques. In the West Fjords, the word hvilft is usually used to refer to a cirque, but this place name is almost unheard of in other parts of the country. Cirque is derived from a

French word used for a circus or amphi-theatre. Anyone walking up into one of the West Fjord cirques will understand exactly why this word is used.

Cirque glaciers form on steep moun-tainsides where snow is able to collect in large volumes, and most of the West Fjord cirques face north – mountainsides fac-ing north receive less sun. During a cold period in an ice age, as the climate cools the "equilibrium line" moves lower down the slopes. Winter snow falling above the equilibrium line does not all melt during the summer. Overhangs of snow form on mountain edges, avalanches fall on the slopes, and thick piles of snow can build up over time in this way. When the ice is thick enough, it begins to flow downwards under its own weight. Along the equilibri-um line, a kind of balance is always main-tained. Above it is the glacier's collection area where the ice is thicker. Glacial creep moves the ice away from the collection area and into the melting zone below the equilibrium line, where it thaws.

Icelandic glaciers all have temperatures close to freezing point and only their sur-face goes below freezing in winter – inside they are wet. At their base or back, cirque glaciers force this water into cracks in the rock. The water freezes and expands inside the cracks, fracturing the rock so that it breaks up. This process is called frost-weathering, and it is particularly ac-tive in Iceland. Using this process the ice digs its way deeper into the mountainside. As it does so, rock collapses onto the high-est part of the glacier where it is buried by fresh snow, and it slides with the glacier, down below the equilibrium line. There, the rock is revealed again on the surface where its sits as a layer of stones lower-most on the snout of the glacier. As the cirque glacier creeps forwards, the highest part may even pull away from the moun-tainside, creating a crevasse by the rock face, called a randkluft. This whole process gradually deepens the bowl. Even though the cirque glaciers actively pluck the rock, the process is slow, and it takes the cirque glaciers a long time to dig their bowl-shaped valleys. The deepest of them were probably formed over a few hundred thou-sand years, which means that they formed over a few glacial periods. What delays the work even more, is that during a glacial maximum the outlet glaciers in the larg-est valleys can become so thick that they "drown" the small cirque glaciers and slow their digging. In fact, the thickness of the main outlet glaciers governs the depth of the cirques. The surface of the large outlet glaciers reached a higher elevation further inland along the fjords and valleys, and this fits well with the fact that the bottoms of cirques, in Skutulsfjörður for example, lie at greater elevations in towards the head of the valley.

But the cirques also have a dark side. Their position makes them ideal snow traps and huge volumes of snow can col-lect in them in winter. Most of them con-tain dangerous avalanche areas, and they must be approached with respect, particu-larly during the winter.

NORTH

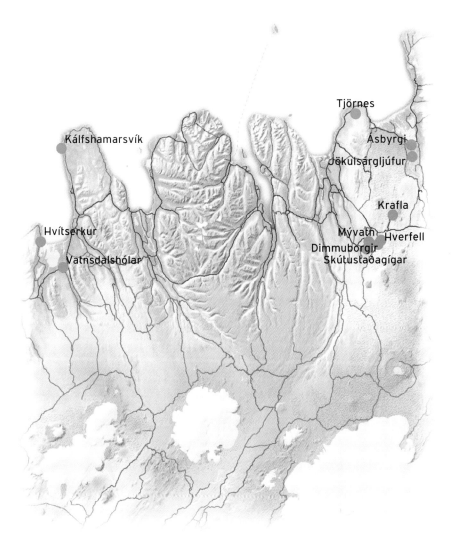

Tjörnes

Kálfshamarsvík

Ásbyrgi

Jökulsárgljúfur

Krafla

Hvítserkur

Mývatn Hverfell

Dimmuborgir

Vatnsdalshólar

Skútustaðagígar

Hvítserkur

Hvítserkur is a distinctive sea stack that stands by the coast, on the east side of the Vatnsnes peninsula. It is about 50 m offshore and surrounded by shallow water. At low tide the water between Hvítserkur and the land is so shallow that it is easily possible to walk out to it and around to either side, without getting wet feet. Hvítserkur (White Shirt) gets its name from its colour; it looks white because of bird droppings. Mainly fulmars and kittiwakes breed there, but some cormorants too.

Hvítserkur is an old dyke, which formed underground when magma flowed into a fracture in the bedrock and filled it. Then the magma solidified and cooled slowly in the fracture. Dykes are frequently supply channels for magma on its way to the surface. The magma that formed the Hvítserkur dyke may have continued all the way to the surface in a fissure eruption, but it might also have been some sort of intrusion along a fissure from a nearby central volcano. Whichever it was, the old land surface has long since eroded away, so we can only see Hvítserkur and where it continues on the coast, towards the south. It is difficult to estimate how much erosion has taken place in the Húnafjörður bay area, but judging by nearby eroded central volcanoes, such as Víðidalsfjall and Vatnsdalsfjall, the bedrock has hardly been eroded less than 500-600 m. So the dyke that we see now as

Hvítserkur originally formed a few hundred metres deep in the earth. When the dyke cooled, the rock fractured into horizontal columns that lie at right angles to the cooling surface. The columns are clearly visible on Hvítserkur and make the formation even more interesting.

Hvítserkur is about 15 m high and similarly wide. It is, however, only between one and two metres thick, so it stands like a big stone slab parallel to the coast. The stack stands on a divided base of rock, which is half submerged at high tide. When the stack is approached, it is possible to see how unstable it is. Over time, the ocean's waves have carved a variety of different sized holes in the lower part of the stack, and the rock appears to stand on three supports. The sea has undercut the northernmost support, the one that faces the ocean, and it tilts to a disconcerting degree relative to the largest portion of the stack. The southernmost support is widest, but it is not actually a natural feature. Until the mid-20th century there were three holes in Hvítserkur, and the southernmost column was in two parts, with a small hole between them. Because of how unstable the stack was, local farmers and other people were worried about the situation, and

in the spring of 1955 a fund was started to save Hvítserkur. The aim was to collect money so that the stack could be strengthened and saved from collapse. Soon afterwards the smallest hole was filled with concrete, and the concrete can clearly be seen in the southernmost support. In 1963, only a few years later, a large earthquake struck north Iceland, which originated in the mouth of the Skagafjörður fjord. The earthquake was felt strongly on Vatnsnes, and some people favoured the idea that the concrete-work had saved Hvítserkur.

It surely has to be thought an unusual step however, to fill in natural features with concrete natural features in order to protect them. Is it normal to hinder the progress of erosion in this way? Does it diminish the value of the features, and would it be done now? Of course it has to be viewed of the period in which it was done - environmental awareness was less than it is today. It is quite likely, though, that the process has already saved Hvítserkur from collapse. So then it is possible to ask yourself, if Hvítserkur had collapsed into the sea mid-century, how many people would now know that it had ever been there?

Vatnsdalshólar

Three natural features in Iceland are regarded as being uncountable – the islands in Breiðafjörður bay, the lakes on the Tvídægra moors and the Vatnsdalshólar hillocks. The last-named features are a vast group of hillocks that can be found in the mouth of the Vatnsdalur valley, near Húnaflói. When you drive the ring-road between Víðigerði and Blönduós, you go across the outskirts of the hillocks. It is perfect to stop there and look at this remarkable feat of nature, which has long been a conundrum for geologists. Several theories have been advanced to explain their formation, but two have endured best and have had most followers through the years. First it was generally thought that the

hillocks were glacial till, left behind by an outlet glacier when it retreated at the end of the last glaciation. The second theory, and the one that most people now think is correct, is that the hillocks were formed in an enormous rockslide from the side of Mt. Vatnsdalsfjall.

The first idea was advanced in the 19th century. Iceland's first geologist, Þorvaldur Thoroddsen, thought that the hillocks had formed towards the end of the last glaciation and were detritus from an Ice Age glacier. He thought that the hillock material had fallen as a scree onto the glacier higher in the valley of Vatnsdalur, and been carried along by the glacier. The glacier had then left the

material behind, in its current position, when it melted. However, in 1936 a local agriculturalist, Jakob Líndal, put forward a new theory about the formation of Vatnsdalshólar in an article in the natural history journal Náttúrufræðingurinn. He thought that the hillocks had formed in an enormous rockslide from the mountain above the valley. Jakob's theory contradicted that previously advanced by Þorvaldur to some extent, but Jakob supported his idea with strong logic. Among other things, Jakob pointed out that the material in the hillocks showed no signs of having been glaciated, as might be expected if an outlet glacier had carried it forwards. Nor did he find any glacial clay in the hillocks, and that would have been a strong indicator of their glacial origin. Jakob studied the area and saw some signs of old beaches, which are indicators of a higher sea level at the end of the last glaciation, both in the valley above Vatnsdalshólar and below. In the Vatnsdalshólar area itself, however, no signs of a higher sea level could be found, and this indicates that the hillocks formed some time after the glaciers retreated and the sea level fell. Finally, Jakob showed that the material in the hillocks was similar to rock in Mt. Vatnsdalsfjall above the hillocks. The westernmost and outermost hillocks are mostly made of basalt, and the principal material in the central portion of hillocks, near the mountain, is rhyolite. Jakob correlated that with the rock strata on the scree-scarred mountain, where the lowermost layers are basalt, with rhyolite above.

This theory of Jakob's has since been widely accepted, but at the end of the 20th century, Þorvaldur's original theory that the hillocks were formed by glacial processes popped up again, that the hillocks were formed by glacial processes. The geologist who suggested this thought that the slopes of Mt. Vatnsdalsfjall showed signs that a glacier had to some degree moved over them, but a rockslide should, on the other hand, have erased such signs. His assessment was that the rhyolite in the centre of the hillocks came from the solid bedrock in the area. In connection with this, he pointed out that dykes can be readily seen in the rhyolite, and they and the rhyolite do not look as though they have moved. Finally, the geologist thought it certain that most of the material in the hillocks was loose material from the Ice Age glacier, and his conclusion was that the loose material in the hillocks had fallen from Mt. Vatnsdalsfjall some distance further up the valley. There it had landed on an outlet glacier that had carried it down and left it behind where the hillocks now stand.

A new article in 2004, however, came to the conclusion that the hillocks were formed in a rock avalanche; rock avalanches can flow exceptionally far from their starting points. In the article it was shown that a glacier played no part in the formation of the hillocks, and a range of supporting evidence was provided. The presence of a striated whaleback (a glaciated rock knoll) can be mentioned here, previously recognised by Jakob Líndal close to the Vatnsdalshólar farm in the middle of the hillocks. At that location the rhyolite core of the hillocks obviously lies on top of the whaleback, making it virtually impossible for it to be part of the area's bedrock. In addition, the dykes in the hillocks have an irregular and haphazard orientation, which argues against them being part of the bedrock. The article therefore adds weight to Jakob Líndal's original theory that the hillocks were formed by a rockslide or rock avalanche, and this has to be thought by far the most likely explanation for their existence.

When the rockslide fell, it may have dammed the valley and created a large lake above the hillocks, although it is also possible that a second rockslide fell later and formed the lake. Over time, that lake became filled in. The current lake, Flóðið, is much younger and was formed by a large rock fall in 1720. In past centuries a number of screes have fallen from Mt. Vatnsdalsfjall, and it could be said that the power of erosion is stronger there than in many other parts of Iceland. No doubt there are many reasons for this, but it is principally the geology of the bedrock and the regional precipitation that makes rock falls common. The bedrock of Mt. Vatnsdalsfjall is unstable for two reasons. Firstly, the remnants of a central volcano can be found there, about six to seven million years old, and the surrounding rock is fractured and hydrothermally altered. Secondly, the rock layers in the mountain

dip (tilt) towards the west, both in towards the old Snæfellsnes-Húnaflói rift zone, and towards the heart of the central volcano. The dip increases the instability of the strata in the mountain, and makes rock falls more likely. As far as precipitation goes, the county of Húnavatnssýsla is drier than other regions. To a large degree this controls the vegetation of the area, and most of the mountainsides are poorly vegetated, lacking any ground cover to bind the soil, reduce the number of screes, and limit the damage they cause. Although the average yearly precipitation is low, there are frequently major downpours in the area, and the soil then becomes saturated. In addition to the general

frost weathering, these conditions all contribute to the formation of scree-falls.

To examine the hillocks and enjoy them in all their glory it is necessary to turn into the Vatnsdalur valley because the hillocks cannot be really appreciated from the main road. The main road used to lie through the hillocks, between the farms of Hólabak and Vatnsdalshólar, giving the traveller a great opportunity to look at the geology. The road was, however, moved to its current position in the mid-20th century. The old road is impassable for vehicles now, but and perfect to walk along it to examine and enjoy the hillocks and their surroundings. On the way, readers can ask themselves if the hillocks are really innumerable. In the summer of 1993, artist Finna Birna Steinsson attempted to count the hillocks. She pushed 1000 pegs with orange flags into the crests of the hillocks to mark each and every one. In the process it became obvious that 1000 pegs were not enough for the job, so the hillocks number at least over 1000. If a brave traveller would like to attempt to find the definitive answer about the number of hillocks it could still be a tricky problem. One question will always arise – what is a hillock, and what isn't a hillock?

Kálfshamarsvík

Kálfshamarsvík is an unfrequented spot on the western side of Skagi, the peninsula between Húnaflói and Skagafjörður. In the early 20th century a small fishing village was built up there; a natural harbour exists in the bay, and it is a short distance to bountiful fishing grounds. The community was at its largest around 1930 when over a hundred people lived there and worked in the fisheries. The community's heyday was short-lived however, and soon after 1940 it was finally abandoned. Now tourists go there mainly to look at traces of the village and enjoy nature. A lighthouse was first erected at Kálfshamarsvík in 1913, but the current lighthouse was built around 1940 and came into operation a few years later. Many people consider the lighthouse to be among the most beautiful buildings in the country; it is similar in shape to several other Icelandic lighthouses.

Walking around Kálfshamarsvík, the history of the community and past fishing culture are close by. So too is the geological history, for those who are interested in it. What first catches your eye, out on the headland by Kálfshamarsvík, are some of the most beautiful columnar basalt formations to be found in Iceland, or even the world. South of the lighthouse is a shallow cove where columns of basalt sweep around the shore, like strings on a harp. The columnar basalt was formed one to two million years ago, and is associated with certain volcanic activity occurring in this area at that time. Most of the bedrock in northwest Iceland, from Hrútafjörður east to Skjálfandaflói, belongs to the Tertiary Period (Neogene) and is between five and twelve million years old. It formed before the Ice Age, and it is the oldest rock on the Tröllaskagi peninsula. About 1.7 mil-

lion years ago, however, volcanic activity began again in Skagafjörður and on Skagi. A new rift zone and volcanic belt formed, stretching from Hofsjökull northwards over the country. This volcanic belt was, however, short-lived and soon became extinct, probably about 0.5 million years ago.

Columnar basalt, like that found at Kálfshamarsvík, is formed by the cooling of thick basalt lavas. Such lavas are fully solidified at around 1000°C, and below this temperature the lava no longer has the elasticity that the magma had. When the lava cools down closer to air temperature, it contracts, but the rock cannot adjust to the contraction and fractures into multiple prisms. Usually the lava forms six-sided prisms when it cools. Hexagonal forms are very common in nature, and this geometry maximises the surface area of the columns relative to the length of the cooling fractures between them. But as most people will find when examining the columnar

basalt are by no means always hexagonal. In many columnar basalt formations, it is possible to find everything from four- to seven-sided columns, and even columns with fewer or more sides.

A lava flow usually cools from the surface down, and the columns always form at right angles to the cooling surface as the lava cools internally. If the lava's cooling surface is horizontal, the columns stand on end, and regular, vertical columnar jointed basalt is formed. Sometimes, however, the cooling can be irregular – if, for example, the lava flows into the sea, or water flows onto it. Then irregular columns form, which can lie at various angles. At Kálfshamarsvík the lava probably flowed into the sea, which resulted in irregular cooling and irregular development of the columns. These formations are similar to those seen in many other places by the sea, for example at Arnarstapi on the Snæfellsnes peninsula.

Skútustaðagígar

On the southwest shore of Lake Mývatn is a small hamlet called Skútustaðir. Farming has been practiced there for centuries, and in recent years substantial services for tourists have been developed. Although many holiday centres in Iceland are in the vicinity of natural beauty spots, there are probably few that equal Skútustaðir, which lies within spitting distance of one of the country's most remarkable natural phenomena. There is no need to walk for more than a few minutes from the car park by the main road to reach the middle of the rootless cones at Skútustaðir. They are among the most beautiful and best-known examples of rootless cones in Iceland, if not the world.

The rootless cones at Mývatn have long fascinated travellers, but at the same time puzzled geologists. Rootless cones can be found widely in Iceland, but the ones surrounding Lake Mývatn are among the largest and shapeliest, and clearly carry the signs of past volcanic activity. About 4000 years ago a vast lava flow issued from a volcano, now called Ketildyngja, southeast of the Mývatn region. The lava has since been named the Older Laxárhraun lava because it ran almost all the way to the sea down the Aðaldalur valley, following the Laxá river. Where the Laxá currently issues from Lake Mývatn, the lava flow dammed the depression around Mývatn. As a result, a lake formed in the depression, a sort of precursor to the Lake Mývatn that we know. About 2000 years later, another lava flow, the Younger Laxárhraun lava, was erupted from a long row of craters named Þrengslaborgir and Lúdentsborgir, over the old Mývatn lake and down the path of the Laxá river. This lava flow fashioned all the present surroundings of Mývatn, and created the rootless cones when the lava flowed into shallow water.

For a long time, various natural scientists thought that rootless cones were eruption craters, formed in some sort of clustered eruption, but others had proposed the idea that they were formed by lava flowing into a marsh or shallow lake. Sigurður Þórarinsson, one of the best-

known Icelandic geologists, described the rootless cones carefully in the mid-20th century, and since then his description has been widely accepted by geologists as the way these features formed. Initially a "runny" lava flows into a shallow lake or marsh. The surface water mostly evaporates, but the ground beneath the lava remains saturated because of groundwater. The lava soon begins to flow in lava tunnels below a solidified lava crust, and the lava flow also thickens, causing increased pressure on the ground beneath the lava. Finally, the molten lava breaks down into the saturated ground, and steam-driven explosions occur when the groundwater suddenly boils. The explosions do not all immediately burst through the overlying lava, but with increasing steam pressure they finally achieve it. A cone builds up above each steam vent, in a sort of explosive eruption which can last for hours, or up to a few days. The size of the cones is dependent on how long the explosive activity lasts, and if the vents are closely spaced, then the cones tend to intersect. Handsome cones have built up widely in Mývatn, but elsewhere in Iceland such eruptions were shorter lived. In Landbrot for example, in southern Iceland, only hillocks were formed, with no crater at the top. The Skútustaðir rootless cones are in

fact so large that the eruptions must have lasted for some time, and lava must have flowed to the cones, from below, during the eruptions. In this way, new material was supplied, and built up these handsome craters.

Because rootless cones are created by steam-driven explosions, it is not unreasonable to say that they erupted. They are sometimes called pseudocraters, meaning false craters, but they are not made by magma rising from the crust below, so they are not formed in the same way as normal volcanic craters. The term "rootless cone" refers to the fact that they are not rooted in a magma conduit in the crust, and this is perhaps a better term because they certainly are craters. The reddish tint of rootless cones is due to oxidation of iron in the cone's material.

As for the formation of Lake Mývatn, after the eruption had ended, groundwater collected behind the wall of lava where the Laxá river now issues. This is how Lake Mývatn was created in its present form, but the rootless cones by the lake provide a very important clue regarding the geological history of the area. By drawing a line around them, it is possible to define the shoreline of the old lake, the lake Mývatn that existed there before the Younger Laxárhraun lava was erupted.

Dimmuborgir

Dimmuborgir is an intriguing and captivating place under the southern slopes of Mt. Hverfell. The "Dark Castles" are a major attraction in the Mývatn region, and for good reason. A walk around the area leads the visitor through dramatic lava formations, a sort of fantasy world peopled by weird beings at every corner. These strange configurations were formed just over two thousand years ago in the largest postglacial eruption of lava in the Mývatn area. It is fascinating for visitors to contemplate the geology of the area when they are at Dimmuborgir - not only because it is so unique, but also because it is so easy to understand the history of the formation and the events that created the place's remarkable setting.

If we go back just over two thousand years, things looked rather different where Dimmuborgir now stands. It is thought that the old lake Mývatn, which most probably formed when the Older Laxárhraun lava was erupted about four thousand years ago, extended a bit further towards the east than the current Mývatn does. Hverfell formed on the edge of the lake, and the lake's shore also lay close to, or even up to, the present Dimmuborgir area. About 2,300 years ago an enormous eruption began in a long fissure east of Hverfell, now called Lúdentsborgir and Þrengslaborgir. The Younger Laxárhraun lava was erupted from these volcanoes; it flowed over the old lake Mývatn and down the Laxá river channel, out to the sea in Skjálfandi bay. A few days after the eruption began, a lava pond formed in a shallow depression about four kilometres, from the volcanoes. Soon after the molten lava collected in the pond, its surface cooled so that a lava crust

formed. The lava, however, continued to flow beneath this surface, into the pond, so the pond deepened from below. This phenomenon is not uncommon in large lava eruptions, as molten lava frequently flows beneath a solidified surface. In the case of Dimmuborgir though, some sort of lava bulge or blister formed, as the lava was lifted up like a balloon being inflated. The rise was greatest in the middle, where the bulge stood 20 metres higher than its surroundings. From the top, the bulge sloped downwards to the edges. In the book *Náttúra Mývatns* this phenomenon is called hraunbóla, which could be translated as "lava zit" – a very descriptive name for it.

Where the lava pond collected was probably a shallow lake or marsh previously. So quite a lot of groundwater was present, and the water began to heat up as soon as the lava flowed over the ground. The steam created forced its way up through the molten lava and formed steam channels around which the lava solidified. This process was not unlike that which formed the rootless cones, but the continuation

and outcome was completely different. It is not clear how long the pond existed, but eventually the blockage gave way and the lava pond emptied. Since the pond surface had already solidified, it collapsed when the rest of the lava drained away. High columns remain to mark where the old steam channels were, and fragments of the solid roof lie scattered among the "castles".

Arriving in Dimmuborgir for a walk, it is good to start by surveying the castles from the viewing disc or service centre. Two things should capture the traveller's attention. First, it is easy to recognise the edge of the old lava pond, especially near to the service centre – the depression that was once full to the brim with molten lava is now vegetated by birch and other shrubs. Second, when viewed from above, it can be seen how the tops of the castles mostly reach the same height, although they are slightly higher in the central area. These two observations fit nicely with the geologists' explanation of how Dimmuborgir formed.

Hverfell

On the eastern side of Lake Mývatn one of the world's largest tephra cones can be seen – formed in a single explosive eruption. At its highest point, this pile of tephra (volcanic ash and larger particles) rises about 170 m above its surroundings. It is about two kilometres in diameter at its base, and its summit holds an enormous crater, over one kilometre across. This mountain is called both Hverfell and Hverfjall, and it has always attracted attention from both tourists and from geologists who have written a lot about it. A walk up Hverfell is a popular activity, and this is not surprising because there is a good view from the top. A pleasant climb becomes even more enjoyable when the formation of the mountain is contemplated, and the enormous eruption which happened there about 3000 years ago.

Research by geologist Sigurður Þorar-insson on the Mývatn area and especially tephra layers from various volcanoes, has had a key role in the interpretation of events there since the last glaciation. Sigurður wrote two important articles about Hverfell in 1952, and was the first person to decide on an age for Hverfell, using two old ash layers erupted by the volcano Hekla, named layers H3 and H4. This was before it was possible to use direct methods for age dating, and Sigurður believed that the upper ash layer, H3, was around 2500-3000 years old. Based on that, he estimated that the Hverfell tephra was about 100-200 years younger, so around 2500-2800 years old. Using carbon-dating methods, H3 has since been dated at 2900 years old, so Sigurður's estimate was almost exactly right.

The formation of Hverfell marks the start of a long period of volcanic activity in

the Krafla area. Although Hverfell seems to stand on its own, it was actually formed in a short fissure eruption. This fissure lay on the edge of a shallow lake, a sort of predecessor of Lake Mývatn. So a lot of water got into the volcano's eruption channel, both lake water and groundwater. When water comes into contact with hot magma, the water suddenly boils and steam-driven explosions occur. In the explosions, the magma is torn to pieces, and it becomes tephra which builds up around the volcanic vent. In the case of Hverfell, this happened over a very short time – based on the pattern made by tephra falling from the volcano, Sigurður estimated that the eruption could hardly have lasted longer than a day or two. He also tried to evaluate the volume of material erupted, and estimated that it was close to half a cubic kilometre of tephra.

In explosive eruptions like this, tephra is spread by the wind, but it is also carried away from the crater by pyroclastic flows. A pyroclastic flow forms from a mixture of tephra and steam, and it behaves like a mudflow when it flows along the ground. Just by the Mývatn Nature Baths, it is possible to see ash layers from Hverfell, formed during pyroclastic flows. In some places it is possible to see prints of tree-trunks in these layers, showing that the countryside was vegetated when the eruption happened. The crater itself was built up by tephra layers. On the outer portion of the crater, the tephra layers slope away from the vent, but they slope inwards on the inner part. On the floor of the crater there is a small tephra cone that probably formed at the end of the eruption when activity had largely diminished.

Judging by the geology, the eruption would certainly have been an amazing sight. Hverfell was declared a protected natural monument in 2011, and according to the protection order it is forbidden to leave the marked hiking trails on the mountain. A hike on the mountain is a unique experience, even more so than many people suspect. Sigurður Þórarinsson wrote in the journal Náttúrufræðingurinn, that although Hverfell may not be the absolutely largest explosion crater on earth, it is one of the most beautifully shaped craters. He classed it with volcanoes such as Mt. Fuji in Japan, in which the volcanic form achieves perfection, he said. It is safe to assume that anyone who has seen Hverfell should be able to agree with Sigurður.

Krafla and Mývatn

For geologists, and perhaps volcanologists in particular, the area around Krafla is without doubt one of the most important areas in Iceland. Krafla is the name of a large central volcano that has probably been active for about 200,000 years. During that period, there has been continual volcanic activity in the area, and an enormous volume of material has been erupted. Krafla's volcanic system stretches quite a distance into the highlands to the south, and it is possible to trace fractures from the volcano northwards into the Öxarfjörður bay. Krafla dominates Lake Mývatn and the surrounding area, and since the end of the last glaciation it has shaped all the area north and east of the lake. With-

in the central volcano itself, is a large and powerful high-temperature geothermal area that has now been harnessed. Volcanic activity in the Krafla system appears to be characterised by periods of frequent eruptions, lasting a few years. The most recent active period, called the Krafla Fires, took place in the years from 1975-84, and it was the largest volcanic outburst in Iceland in the last century.

Krafla was one of the most-researched geological areas in Iceland in the 20th century, and this was due to a few factors. It is a large area and relatively accessible from the nearest settlements. One of Iceland's first geothermal power stations was built

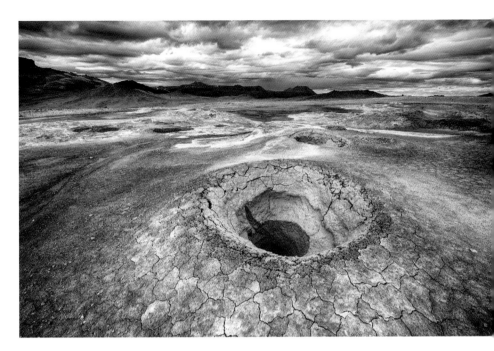

there, and the Krafla Fires were also incredibly exciting and interesting in the eyes of earth scientists. A considerable amount has been written about the area. The volcanologist Sigurður Þórarinsson must of course be mentioned here – he laid the foundations for our present understanding of Krafla's eruptive history.

The volcanic features of the Krafla system are from the last two glacial stages of the most recent ice age. During those periods tuyas (table mountains) were built up under the ice, and in the warmer interglacial stages, lava shields and lava flows were erupted. A large portion of this erupted material is now hidden by younger formations, so the early history of the system is patchy. However, it is known that just after the end of the last interglacial stage, around 100,000 years ago, a caldera formed in a large explosive eruption, but the caldera has been largely filled since then. As we get closer to our own time the picture becomes clearer though, and

the eruptive history from the end of the last glaciation is fairly well known. In postglacial times (Holocene) volcanic activity has been divided into two main episodes. The first episode began some time at the end of the last glacial stage, and ended about 8000 years ago. Many volcanic features from this period have been recognised east of Lake Mývatn, such as the explosive crater called Lúdent, eruptive fissures and lava at Mt. Námafjall, and an old lava associated with Kröfluháls. After the end of this earlier volcanic episode, identified with the crater Lúdent, volcanic activity stopped for about 5000 years – with the exception of one minor event in the middle of the break.

The Krafla system started up again about 3000 years ago when a new volcanic episode, identified with Mt. Hverfell, began, and most of the best-known formations at Mývatn are from this period. However, a little before the start of the Hverfell episode, about 4000 years ago, there was an eruption in the volcanic system south of Krafla, called the Fremrinámur system. There was an eruption in the Ketildyngja lava shield, and a vast lava flow was erupted, called the Older Laxárhraun lava. It is thought to have flowed more than 80 km down the Laxá river channel in Aðaldalur to the lowlands. The lava flow probably dammed the river Laxá and created an early version of Lake Mývatn in the low-lying Mývatn area. In contrast, Krafla's second period of postglacial activity began with an enormous explosive eruption on the edge of this early Lake Mývatn, during which Mt. Hverfell was formed. Although Hverfell towers alone over its surroundings, it is in fact part of a 1800 m long eruptive fissure. In all, a 25 km section of the fissure erupted in the Hverfell event, and the fissure stretched north of Krafla's caldera. Lavas from this eruption originally covered about 70 km^3 of land, but a large portion of them now lies beneath younger lavas. With the exception of Mt. Hverfell, it is easiest to examine signs of this volcanic episode at Jarðbaðshólar, the craters by the Mývatn Nature Baths.

The next volcanic episode occurred about 2000 years ago. There was an eruption in the northern part of the Krafla volcanic system, but at a similar time there was another episode to the south and east of Mývatn. There was an eruption in the Lúdent and Þrengsla

crater rows (Þrengslaborgir and Lúdentsborgir) and also in the Grænavatn crater row. Sigurður Þórarinsson named the lava flow from these eruptions the Younger Laxárhraun lava. In fact, most geologists agree that based on its chemistry, the Younger Laxárhraun lava was not erupted from within the Krafla system itself, but in a separate system just to the south of it, called Heiðarsporð. This eruption was the largest postglacial lava eruption in the Mývatn area, and the Younger Laxárhraun lava covers 220 km^2. In all, the eruptive fissures were about 16.5 km long, but possibly the Grænavatn crater row erupted somewhat before the Lúdent and Þrengsla crater rows, so it may not have been part of the same event. The time between the eruptions was so short that it is not possible to differentiate between them by age-dating. The Younger Laxárhraun lava flowed down the Laxá river channel, and covers a large part of the Older Laxárhraun lava all the way to coast in Skjálfandi bay. The current landscape and the environs of Mývatn were largely shaped in this eruption. Most of the floor of the lake was created in the eruption, rootless cones and all sorts of lava features in addition to the Dimmuborgir area itself.

Since this massive outburst of activity, there have been a few eruptive episodes in the volcanic system. After the settlement of Iceland there have been two fairly large volcanic episodes in the Krafla system. The first one took place in 1724-29 and has been called the Mývatn Fires. The Mývatn Fires began with an explosive eruption in which the crater Víti was formed. After this, eruptions occurred in a few places along an approximately 13 km long section west of Víti. The volume of lava from these eruptions varied, but most was erupted in the summer of 1729 when lava flowed from the volcanoes above the populated area, and destroyed three farms there. That lava flow is called

Eldhraun, and it forms the western boundary of the hamlet Reykjahlíð, by Lake Mývatn.

After the end of the Mývatn Fires, activity more or less ceased until the middle of the last century. In 1974 work began on the construction of the Krafla Power Station, a geothermal power plant that was to utilise steam from boreholes in the Krafla area. In December 1975, however, an eruption began at Leirhnúkur. That small eruption marked the start of the Krafla Fires, and they were to continue until September 1984. During these nine years there were a total of nine eruptions, in addition to considerable underground movement of magma. This caused a lot of controversy regarding the Krafla Power Station since not everyone agreed about continuing in view of the risks associated with the eruptions. The volcanic activity in the cycle can be split in two, based on the nature of the eruptions. In the early years until March 1980, the eruptions were small and lasted only a few hours each. However, the later eruptions were larger, and lasted one or two weeks. A considerable volume of lava was erupted in them, and some of it was erupted along 8-9 km long fissures. In total, lava from the Krafla Fires covers about 35 km^2 and has a volume of about 4 km^3. The Krafla Fires are thought to have been similar in size to the Mývatn Fires.

The Krafla Fires were of great importance to geoscientists. For the first time there was an opportunity to study magma movement and the formation of dykes underground, with the help of seismometers. Land inflation was also measured in the lead-up to the eruptions, and subsidence after activity ceased. Most remarkable of all were measurements of rifting in the Krafla central volcano - the crust there separated by about five metres in only a few years. From this it has been concluded that rifting in the Krafla volcanic system is associated with eruptive episodes occurs infrequently in between them.

N

Tjörnes

If asked to name one place in Iceland of greatest importance for studying the earth's past, doubtless many would think of Tjörnes. On the west coast of the peninsula, in inlets and gullies north of Húsavík and all the way to Tjörnestá, some of the world's most remarkable strata (rock layers) can be found. From these beds, geologists have not only read the changes in oceanic temperature over the last millions of years, but also the history of the Ice Age, almost in its entirety. For those who want to study this history, a daytrip on the Tjörnes peninsula can be fascinating and astonishing. Over a distance of only a few kilometres, it is possible to walk through 1.5 million years of climate change

history on Earth, and on the tip of the peninsula, multiple layers of glacial sediments and lavas alternate in a way hardly matched anywhere else in the world.

The Tjörnes beds can be divided into four main groups of rock. The oldest rocks are lavas, named after Kaldakvísl, a river just north of Húsavík. The Köldukvíslarhraun lavas are the oldest part of Tjörnes and north of them lie increasingly younger rocks. Near the river Kaldakvísl are the oldest rock layers containing shells and beds of soft coal called lignite. These are the "real" Tjörnes beds, although this name is often used for all the strata on the peninsula. The Tjörnes beds lie from Kalda-

66

kvísl, north to Höskuldsvík bay. There, the Höskuldsvíkurhraun lavas take over, and then the Breiðavík beds appear in an inlet further north. In the Breiðavík beds are many alternating layers of lava and glacial sediments, and they stretch all the way north to Tjörnestá, east of which younger lavas take over. Within these main groups are some lesser groups, such as the Furuvík beds, named after another inlet, and minor lava flows.

The ages of these beds have been dated by various methods; before the mid-20th century, direct age measurements were not possible. So all age dates were made relative to other strata, elsewhere in Iceland or the world. Different geologists could make quite different decisions about the relative ages, but when direct methods of dating were developed, it was possible to discover the real ages of the rock. Direct dating methods are based on the ratios of radioactive substances in the rocks. Some natural elements are radioactive and break down to other forms over time. Most of these decay processes are fairly or very well known, and if it is possible to measure the ratios of the elements in the strata then it is possible to calculate how long it is since the rocks formed. Some radioactive substances are more suitable than others for this work, depending on both the age and the type of the rock. Organic material plant and animal remains, can be age dated by radiocarbon dating, but this only works on remains less than 50,000 years old. Since the rocks on Tjörnes containing fossils are all older than this, radiocarbon dating is impossible. For older strata other elements must be used, such as uranium and potassium, although these are present in only small quantities in Icelandic basalt. For many years it was difficult to date the lavas on Tjörnes, but over time it has proved possible to develop a fairly reliable picture of how the rock layers built up.

The Köldukvíslarhraun lavas are thought to be between 8.5 and 10 million years old, while the oldest lava layer in the Tjörnes shell beds is about 4 to 5 million years old. So, between the formation of the Köldukvíslarhraun lavas and the Tjörnes beds, over four million years went by. During this period other layers of rock were almost certainly deposited, but for some reason there is no sign of them now. When this sort of thing happens, geologists call it an "unconformity", and it is equivalent to removing a few chapters from the earth's geological history. Sometimes geologists are able to fill in the gaps, but more often we have no real idea what happened. By crossing the small river Kaldakvísl, we are actually jumping over a few million years of Earth history.

On the far side of Kaldakvísl, the Tjörnes beds take over. They are usually divided into three zones, based on which fossils are most common in the layers of rock. Furthest south is the Tapes zone, named after the three species of carpet shell commonly found in it. Nowadays, carpet shells are common around the British Isles, and they are also found all the way from Norway's coast south to Morocco. Research on the shells suggests that when the Tapes beds were deposited, the sea temperature around Iceland was up to 10°C higher than it is now. At the river Reká, the shell fauna changes when the carpet shells disappear and new shells belonging to the species Mactra appears. This species of shell is now extinct, but other shells found along with it in the Mactra zone indicate that the sea temperature was at least 5°C higher than it is now. However, research on the shells indicates that the air temperature was changeable at this time, and the climate was cooling.

On the coast by the Hallbjarnarstaðaá river, another change in the shell fauna occurs – the Greenland cockle dominates

in the Serripes zone. Other warm-water species also disappear from the rocks, and the shells that now live around Tjörnes appear for the first time in the sedimentary beds. This change is sometimes accepted as indicating the beginning of the Ice Age, although the sea temperature was for a long time very similar to what it is now. Another very important change is where a number of shell species originating in the Pacific Ocean suddenly appear in the Serripes zone. The existence of these species in the beds is thought to indicate the opening of the Bering Strait between Alaska and Siberia – a major event in the earth's geological history. The presence of the shells in the Tjörnes beds suggests that when they were being deposited, a relatively shallow marine environment dominated at Tjörnes. However, beds of lignite can be found in between the shell sediments, and this indicates that the land rose temporarily above sea level and then sank again. It is easiest to look at the Tjörnes beds by driving down to the sea

by Hallbjarnarstaðaá, just north of the farm Ýtri-Tunga. For those who want to examine the Tjörnes beds as completely as they can, then it is possible to go down to them at the Kaldakvísl river and walk by the sea, north to Hallbjarnarstaðaá. Those who want to undertake this must, however, be prepared to wade across a few rivers on the way.

Lava take over at the Höskuldsvík inlet, lying above the Serripes beds, and further north, layers of sedimentary rock are found at Furuvík and Breiðavík. At Breiðavík numerous layers of lava alternate with glacial sediments called tillites. Lava flowed down to the sea in warmer interglacial periods during the Ice Age, and the tillites were formed during glacial periods. Preservation of these rocks is really due to the interplay of glaciers and volcanoes because the lava, which was erupted in interglacial periods, covered the older tillites and protected them from the glaciers. For this reason, there is nowhere else on Earth where so many tillites are found together in one rock formation – a total of nine or ten tillites have been identified at Breiðavík. It is best to examine these beds by walking along the cliffs at Breiðavík, from south to north. The beds end at Tjörnestá, where dramatically dark lava appears abruptly on top of the sediments in the cliffs. A more fitting end to a geological trip on the peninsula is hard to imagine.

The Tjörnes beds are well known among geologists the world over, particularly among sedimentary geologists and palaeontologists, and the beds have been much studied by both Icelandic and scientists from overseas. And no wonder, because they provide a unique opportunity to read the history of the earth with the help of fossils – Iceland has a poor fossil record compared to other countries, generally speaking. These studies have focussed fairly evenly on the fossils, sedimentary rocks, and the ages of the strata. But although an enormous amount of work has been done, it is always possible to do more, and hopefully future geologists will continue to seek out the Tjörnes beds.

Given the significance of the Tjörnes beds for geological history, both in Iceland and the world, it is very strange that the area has not been given protected status. The shells and sediments are definitely interesting to the public, and there are also other remarkable features on the peninsula, such as the coastal waterfall on the river Skeifá, the enormous rock brought by an iceberg from Greenland, and signs of lignite mining dating from the First World War. Protection is not only necessary to preserve the geological features – its role is also to highlight the importance of a place. Conservation is a sort of acknowledgement of the significance of the location, and the necessity to treat the area with respect and humility. The Tjörnes beds span a very important period in the history of the Earth. The arrival of the Ice Age played a major part in human biological evolution and the Tjörnes beds record details of that period in a unique way.

Jökulsárgljúfur and Ásbyrgi

Some of Iceland's most magnificent landscapes can be seen at the head of Öxarfjörður bay, in the district known as Norður-Þingeyjarsýsla. The river Jökulsá á Fjöllum flows to the sea in Öxarfjörður, and it divides the land adjoining the bay in two - the district to the west of the river is called Kelduhverfi. Jökulsá á Fjöllum is one of the largest rivers in Iceland, and its source comes from two of Vatnajökull's outlet glaciers, Dyngjujökull and Brúarjökull. Jökulsá is 206 km long, and the water is nearly two days on the way from the glacier to the sea. The river flows through one of the most volcanically active parts of Iceland, and all its surroundings are marked by this. Its upper part flows over black desert sands on the edge of the Ódáðahraun lava field, but around 50 km from the coast it suddenly drops down from the edge of the central highlands, into the deep Jökulsárgljúfur canyon. There, it tumbles along between high cliffs in one of the most magnificent canyons in the country, surrounded by beautiful rock formations and vegetation which is virtually unrivalled. Next to the mouth of this canyon is another impressive canyon called Ásbyrgi. The cliff walls of Ásbyrgi are up to 100 m high, and the mouth of the canyon is divid-

ed in two by an island-like crag called Eyja, which is 60 m high. In 1973 a national park was established around Jökulsárgljúfur, and Ásbyrgi was added soon after. Now the area is all part of Vatnajökull National Park.

Unlike many magnificent places elsewhere in Iceland, the landscape at Jökulsárgljúfur has only suffered minor glaciation, although the distant Vatnajökull icecap undoubtedly dominates the area indirectly. This area has been influenced much more by volcanic activity and the huge roaring river that has carved through the bedrock. About 25 km south of where the edge of the lava is at Kelduhverfi, there is a crater called Stóravíti. Around 11,000-12,000 years ago one of the country's largest lava eruptions occurred, and an enormous lava shield was formed, all the way east to the current path of the Jökulsá river. The cliff walls at Ásbyrgi are made of this lava torrent, as is the northernmost part of Jökulsárgljúfur. After this eruption the Ice Age glaciers briefly overran the area again before finally retreating. A little later, about eleven thousand years ago, there was another eruption, but this time to the east of where the River Jökulsá now flows. Signs of this eruption can be seen at

many places along the canyon and eruptive vents are at two locations – at Hljóðaklettar and Rauðhólar, and somewhat further south at Randarhólar. The Jökulsá has eroded these volcanoes and broken them wide open, both during and after the eruption.

In the Vesturdalur valley are the Hljóðaklettar cliffs – beautiful and very irregularly jointed remains of a crater row, the continuation of which can be seen to the north as the scorched and reddened Rauðhólar. The irregular columnar jointing at Rauðhólar indicates that water was involved, and it cooled the lava in the crater centres in various ways. Later, the river removed all the scoria (cinders) on the outside of them. By neatly peeling away the outsides of the Hljóðaklettar craters and leaving those at Rauðhólar almost untouched, Nature has written a textbook in volcanology, easier and more fun to read than anything written by humans. Just below the Dettifoss waterfall, the river Jökulsá cuts through another crater row of similar age to Hljóðaklettar. This crater row is usually identified with the previously mentioned Randarhólar, just north of the river, but in fact it is part of the longest crater row in Iceland, and belongs to the Askja volcanic system. The Jökulsá cascades over Hafragilsfoss at about the same place as the river cuts through the craters, and it is possible to view them on both sides of the river. If arriving at Hafragilsfoss from the west, an unusual sight can be seen in the cliff wall on the far side of the river, at Sjónnípa. The conduit that fed one of the craters can be seen there as a black tube, several metres wide, and it is easy to see how the magma pushed its way through the rock layers. Shortly after the eruption, the river eroded the eruptive crater "to the bone", so to speak, and it is rare to get such a good view of the interior of a volcano.

But how has the river Jökulsá managed to erode such a magnificent canyon in the time since the last glaciation? The canyon is about 30 km long and in many places so wide that it seems more like a valley than a canyon. At Dettifoss it is possible to see how the canyon formed. In a half-kilometre-long section below the waterfall, the canyon is narrow, and the river there descends enclosed between the cliff walls. Clearly an active canyon-forming process is taking place there, in which the river steadily erodes the waterfall's edge. Downstream of this narrow section, the course widens suddenly, and it is obvious that, giving the current flow rate, the river has not been large enough to erode such a wide channel. To better understand the canyon-forming process in this location we need to look more closely at flow rates in a glacial river like Jökulsá á Fjöllum.

As is usual in a glacial river, the flow rate is many times higher in summer months than in winter. On warm summer days, when there is most sun-melted water on the glaciers, the flow rate can be up to seven or eight times more than the average winter flow. There are also regular outburst floods of various origins. Floods of slushy ice happen occasionally, especially in spring, when an ice dam builds up and the river channel fills, often over quite a short time. In the case of Jökulsá á Fjöllum, scientists have also pointed out a risk of glacial outburst floods due to volcanic activity in Vatnajökull. It is believed that several such floods occurred in the 17th and 18th centuries. These floods are so large that their power to erode is much more then that of the river under normal conditions. The formation of the canyon system is, however, connected to a much bigger flood than those which we are familiar with. In 1973 two articles were published by Icelandic geologists Haukur Tómasson and Kristján Sæmundsson. They put forward the theory that a "catastrophic flood" in Jökulsá á Fjöllum had eroded the canyon and Ásbyrgi. In a catastrophic flood the erosive power of a river system is so enormous that it can cut through bedrock as if it were butter. This is because of the high flow-rate of the flood water - in fast-flowing water the water pressure can drop so much that vapour bubbles form in the water. When the bubbles burst, they emit shock waves which shatter the surrounding rock. This important process is called cavitation. Because these floods happened before the settlement of Iceland, they can only be detected by the signs they left behind. Haukur thought that one such flood had eroded the area about 2000–3000 years ago, and he based his theory on research by volcanologist Sigurður Þórarinsson about the ages of different ash layers. Sigurður had previously shown that in old channels of the Jökulsá, above Ásbyrgi for example, the roughly 3000-year-old ash layer that had been erupted from Hekla was missing, but a 2000-year-old ash layer was present. This meant that all ash layers older than 2000 years had been swept away somehow, and this provided justification for the suggested age of the cataclysmic flood. Kristján agreed that a large flood had poured down the Jökulsá channel at this time, but he thought that an even bigger flood was largely responsible for eroding the canyon and Ásbyrgi earlier, close to the end of glaciation. Some arguments tend to support Kristján's version more than Haukur's, that more than one flood came down the channel, and that the channel was even eroded to a large extent in the late glacial period. In re-

cent years some geologists have wanted to go even further, and proposed that Ásbyrgi and a lot of the Jökulsárgljúfur canyon actually formed beneath a glacier, just after the ice advanced over the new lava shield erupted from Stóravíti. They have justified this by pointing to glacial striations (scratches made by glaciers) in the flood path above Ásbyrgi – such marks would have been washed away in a cataclysmic flood. They have also pointed out signs of old beaches 30 metres above the present sea level on Eyja, the big crag at Ásbyrgi, and dated them to the late glacial period. Like the glacial striations, the raised beaches would hardly have survived a cataclysmic flood.

From these various speculations by geologists, it is clear that there is still a need for definitive research on the origins of the Jökulsárgljúfur canyon and Ásbyrgi. Judging by the signs though, there have probably been a few cataclysmic floods down the path of Jökulsá á Fjöllum, and the maximum flow rate in the largest flood is even thought to have reached about a million cubic metres per second. The best thing about these speculations though, is that visitors can travel around the area and check how the different theories fit with what they see. They may discover something new and unexpected in connection with the history of how the canyon formed. If that happens, it is important that the new ideas are made public, so that we can get a little closer to the truth.

E

Dyrfjöll and Stórurð

Helgustaðir mine

Snæfell

Teigarhorn

Jökulsárlón and Breiðamerkurjökull

Öræfájökull

Dyrfjöll and Stórurð

When driving north from Egilsstaðir to Borg-arfjörður Eystri, one of Iceland's more beautiful mountain ranges lies before you. In the middle of the row, a rather odd feature can be seen, looking like an enormous notch, or "door" in the rock wall. These are the Dyrfjöll mountains, considered by many to be the most majestic of all the mountains in the region. Like so many other features in Iceland, the Dyrfjöll mountains, with their sharp edges and steep rock faces, were shaped by Ice Age glaciers that tirelessly moved over the country and eroded it. Unlike most other places though, here the Ice Age glacier left an unusually magnificent parting gift when it disappeared from Dyrfjöll at the end of the last glaciation. West of the "door", there is a peculiar place that has been named Stórurð. Enormous boulders lie scattered there. They are rocks that the glacier was struggling to move down from the mountains when it

suddenly retreated at the end of the last glaciation, about ten to eleven thousand years ago.

The Ice Age glacier thus has a key role in the formation of the Dyrfjöll mountains as seen today. A few ice-streams issued from the mountains, both to the east and west, and two of these streams of ice met at the "door" and cut a gap in the mountain. But the story is only half told at this point, because the geology of the area is much more complicated. Around Dyrfjöll, many volcanic features can be seen – about 12-13 million years ago this area was in the middle of an active central volcano, the Dyrfjöll central volcano. In fact, the whole area in the mountains around Borgarfjörður Eystra and all the way south to Loðmundarfjörður is unusually rich in beautiful formations. In addition to the Dyrfjöll mountains, there are others, such as Svartfell, Skúmhöttur

and Hvítserkur. Unfortunately, few people have studied the area in detail, and a lot of geological research still needs to be done.

The lifetime of the Dyrfjöll central volcano has been divided into five stages, and these stages are comparable to those of many other central volcanoes, both active and extinct. First, a low volcano forms when primitive basalt lava begins to flow. In time the volcano reaches the next stage, when it starts to erupt differentiated, more acidic lava. In the third stage the main build-up of the volcano from basalt lava takes place, but eventually things begin to decline, and the fourth stage signals the beginning of the end – an enormous explosive eruption suddenly happens, and the roof of the volcano collapses, creating a large caldera. The caldera is gradually filled by younger lavas that finally drown the volcano. It seems to be the inevitable fate of every Icelandic volcano to be buried by younger lava flows.

The best way to see the structure of the Dyrfjöll central volcano is by looking at it from the top down, even though you could say that this is starting at the wrong end. It is easy to see that the upper part of the Dyrfjöll mountains is made from many layers of basalt that lie one on top of the other, with occasional red layers in between. These are the youngest lavas; the ones that lie on top of the remains of the volcano. Below the lava, on the other hand, unusual layers of rock can be seen, much lighter in colour than the lava and less compact. These are layers of ignimbrite – a type of rock that forms in huge explosive eruptions. Here, the next-to-last stage of the Dyrfjöll volcano is revealed. The ignimbrite formed when material ejected in an explosive eruption fell back into the caldera, partially filling it. In many places around Dyrfjöll, rocks from other stages of the volcano can be recognised, and it is interesting to look at those formations. You could say that together, Dyrfjöll and Stórurð constitute one of the most amazing areas of Iceland, and hardly anyone who visits them will remain unmoved.

Helgustaðir Mine

Sometime between 1668 and 1669, the Danish doctor and mathematician Rasmus Bartholin received an unusual mineral specimen from Iceland. The sample came to him via King Frederick III of Denmark – the king to get wind unusual crystals in Iceland and in 1668, ordered that a stonemason be sent to the country to collect them. The Icelandic crystals were transparent and so clear that it was possible to see through them. Bartholin examined the crystal samples and, among other things, he tried placing them over a black dot on a sheet of paper. It was easy to make out the dot through the crystals, but strangely the dot appeared to be double when seen through the sample. And moreover, one of dots seemed to move in a circle around the other if the sample was rotated. Bartholin had discovered something called double refraction, the splitting of a light ray into two rays, and he subsequently studied the crystals in detail. In 1669 he published an important scientific paper about his experiments in double refraction using the Icelandic crystals. His essay has sometimes been named one of the two essays that established crystallography as a science. After Bartholin's discovery, other scientists studied and wrote about double refraction in the Icelandic crystals, and the most important of them were probably physicists Christiaan Huygens and Sir Isaac Newton. Writings by the world famous scientists marked the beginning of an active role for "Iceland spar" from Helgustaðir in the history of science.

However, it took a long time for science to ascertain the nature of light, even though the Iceland spar, a form of calcite,

was a great help. The history and role of calcite from the Helgustaðir mine, through to the 20th century, is remarkable, and its influence on science has been important in three main areas. Firstly, there is the direct involvement of Iceland spar in many scientific discoveries. These were discoveries that helped scientists move in the right direction in various scientific fields such as optics, crystallography, mineralogy, physics and biology. Secondly, Iceland spar was used widely as a teaching aid in all sorts of discussions about the properties of materials and crystals, and in optics. Finally, the role of Iceland spar in various experiments involving polarised light was significant. Around 1830 William Nicol was the first person to make a simple polariser out of Iceland spar, called the Nicol prism. It was in use until the 20th century, in microscopes and other scientific instruments. So the Danish king's original interest in a pretty stone was to have an immeasurable impact on science.

Although Iceland spar was discovered in the latter half of the 17th century, it was not until the 19th century that scientists became seriously interested in it. After around 1800, scientists began to wrestle with theories about the nature of light, and progress was subsequently rapid in that field. Demand for Iceland spar increased at the same time, but until 1850 the calcite mine was small. Scientists, naturalists, and other visitors passing through that part of the country usually stopped at Helgustaðir and collected Iceland spar for export. Organised mining began about 1850 when a businessman from Seyðisfjörður obtained permission from the land owner to mine and sell the calcite abroad. After that, production increased, and a considerable quantity of Iceland spar was excavated until 1872 when mining ceased. A period of uncertainty took over regarding the mine, during which little calcite was produced, but mining began again after about 1895. The mine never again achieved its previous levels of production though, and the quality of the calcite declined. A few very

large crystals were, however, dug from the mine in the 1880s and 1890s. Some of them weighed as much as 200-300 kg.

Iceland spar was mined at Helgustaðir until the First World War when work temporarily stopped. Until then the material had been worked straight from the hillside, gradually creating a large pit. In 1920 the Icelandic government employed a recently graduated Icelandic mining engineer to get production going again. In the summer of 1921 he initiated tunnelling beneath the old mine, and mining went on there until 1924. Work stopped that year, and by then the tunnel was 70-80 m long. Minor amounts of calcite were mined after that, but the last calcite was removed in 1946-47.

This important period in the history of science began much further back, of course, than any written records. The geological history of the calcite in the Helgustaðir mine is no less important than its role in the history of science. It could be said that the Iceland spar at Helgustaðir owes its existence to a large central volcano at Reyðarfjörður

– it was active about 10-11 million years ago. As is often the case in such central volcanoes, a large number of dykes were intruded. This dyke swarm stretched from the Reyðarfjörður volcano, north to Mjóifjörður. Hydrothermal activity is generally associated with such dyke emplacement, and hot water flows through the rock and dissolves various chemicals from it. The hydrothermal fluid carries the chemicals away, and they precipitate out and form new secondary minerals somewhere else in the rock. The area now on the north side of the Reyðarfjörður inlet provided, for some reason, perfect conditions for the formation of particularly large and pure secondary minerals. The Iceland spar at Helgustaðir obviously follows a large dyke in the area, and amygdales (vesicles filled with secondary minerals) can also be found in the rock surrounding the dyke. So the dyke has played the role of a hydrothermal channel, with the hydrothermal fluid flowing upwards along it.

The crystals formed from calcium (Ca) and carbon dioxide (CO_2) dissolved by hot water in the rock – together they make calcium carbonate ($CaCO_3$). Calcium carbonate can crystallise in various ways, but at Helgustaðir it has produced a very clear form of calcite which breaks into rhombohedrons, or "squashed" cubes. In Icelandic it is called silfurberg, which means "silver-rock", but it is not related to actual silver. In other countries it was originally called Icelandic crystals (Crystalli Islandici), but in the 19th century the name Iceland spar (isländischer Doppelspat, spath d'Islande) stuck to the crystals, and although Iceland spar was subsequently found in other parts of the world, its name in many languages still links it to Iceland.

It should not be forgotten that until the start of the 20th century, all the Iceland spar in the scientific world came from a single mine, the one at Helgustaðir. No other important Iceland spar mine was discovered until part way into the century, so the scientific world was totally dependent on Icelandic calcite until then. In the light of this, it is strange that the story of Iceland spar has not been more widely disseminated over the years, because Iceland spar is one of Iceland's greatest contributions to the scientific community. Léo Kristjánsson, an Icelandic geophysicist who has done most research into the history of Iceland spar, believes that the Iceland spar mine at Helgustaðir might possibly be the most important locality for giant calcite crystals in the world. It is therefore incumbent on the authorities to improve conditions at the site, and give Helgustaðir the recognition it deserves. In 1975 the Helgustaðir mine was protected as a "natural monument", and it is forbidden to collect samples of Iceland spar there – even though visitors have chosen to ignore this directive all too often over the years. Things need to be better managed. Facilities at the Helgustaðir mine need to be improved and adequately maintained. Following this, it would be best to begin preparations to nominate Helgustaðir to the UNESCO World Heritage List because of its cultural significance – the Helgustaðir mine undoubtedly deserves to be included.

Snæfell

Snæfell is the highest mountain in Iceland besides of the large icecaps, and it is also one of the highest volcanoes in the country. It is a stratovolcano which has probably been active for a few hundred thousand years – the oldest lavas at the base of the mountain have been dated at around 300-400 thousand years old. The mountain has built up gradually over that time period, although a considerable length of time has usually passed between eruptions. The main part of the mountain has built up around one central crater at its summit, but there are many other volcanic features in the area, such as móberg (hyaloclastite) formations, that were formed at the same time as the mountain. Mt. Snæfell and its volcanic nature have long been somewhat puzzling for geologists, and there are two reasons for this. Firstly, it has proved difficult to connect the volcano to Iceland's volcanic belts and other volcanoes, and secondly, no conclusion has been reached as to whether the volcano is active or not.

Lava and other material erupted from Snæfell have been studied and dated, and the youngest age-dated material from Snæfell is about 190,000 years old. However, at the top of the mountain are lavas that seem to have been minimally worn or eroded by glacial action, which points towards a young age, possibly to an eruption having occurred in the volcano after the last glaciation ended. If this is so, then Snæfell is probably an active volcano, since volcanoes are classed as active if they have erupted since the end of the last glaciation – but geologists do not all agree about this. Snæfell is obviously not a volcano in its most active phase though, since few young formations are found in and around it. Generally speaking, Icelandic central volcanoes are a half to one million years old before they become completely extinct and drift away from the active rift zone. In Snæfell's case the picture is not that simple because Snæfell does not lie on the active rift zone, but rather on some sort of side belt

to the east of the North Volcanic Zone. This volcanic belt is entirely on the Eurasian tectonic plate, so no drift is involved. Usually two other volcanoes, Öræfajökull and Esjufjöll, are considered to be on this volcanic belt. The chemical composition of material erupted from Snæfell and Öræfajökull indicate some similarity between them, but the Esjufjöll volcanic system has been studied very little, and its status and activity level is unclear.

It is possible that the volcanic belt which connects Öræfajökull and Snæfell is an indicator of a future active rift zone. It is often called a "flank zone", and it currently lies some distance east of the mantle plume underlying Iceland. Since the Icelandic tectonic plates are drifting slowly northwest relative to the mantle plume the flank zone could actually end above the mantle plume. If that is the future, then the Öræfajökull and Snæfell flank zone is a sort of precursor to a future rift zone.

It is not just volcanic activity and its relationship with Iceland's volcanic zones that make Snæfell interesting, though. Because the mountain is so high, it has a summit glacier, and a number of glaciers flow down the sides. These glaciers are, however, more unusual than most because of their appearance – many of them are what is called debris-covered glaciers, glaciers that have so much rock and sand mixed in with the ice that they look completely black. In spite of the rock detritus these glaciers still flow downwards, but more slowly than most others. Four glaciers on Snæfell have names, and they are fairly descriptive of their appearance. They are called Dökkurðarjökull (Dark-debris Glacier), Ljósurðarjökull (Pale-debris Glacier), Axlarjökull (Shoulder Glacier), and the fourth glacier is called either Hálsjökull (Neck Glacier) or Sótajökull (Soot Glacier). Dökkurðarjökull and Ljósurðarjökull are the largest, and they descend to the plain northwest of Snæfell. The tongues of both of these glaciers are completely covered by debris and rock from the mountain, so you would have to walk for a kilometre alongside the glaciers before seeing white glacial ice.

Hiking on Snæfell is challenging, although specialised ice-climbing gear or mountaineering experience is only required in winter. In good weather, the view from the mountain is unforgettable – Snæfell towers over the surrounding highland plateau and there are great vistas towards the East Fjords, the Egilsstaðir area and north to Jökuldalsheiði.

Teigarhorn

Natural scientists from other countries have long been fascinated by Iceland's geology and nature; indeed, it is exotic compared to what many are used to in their homeland. Various places in Iceland have achieved fame among foreign geologists, and some locations have become virtually world famous. These include the Helgustaðir mine in Reyðarfjörður, and Teigarhorn in Berufjörður, East Iceland. From the end of the 18th century until the 20th, Teigarhorn was probably one of the most famous geological locations in the country, but unfortunately it has now been largely forgotten. What made Teigarhorn famous were its beautiful and decorative stones, called zeolites. Zeolites are a group of secondary minerals that form when hydrothermal fluid passes through basalt lava, deep beneath the surface of the ground. There are many types of zeolites, and they are found in many places in the world, but at Teigarhorn some of the world's largest and most beautiful specimens can be found.

The zeolites at Teigarhorn are found as amygdales (filled holes) in the lavas around the locality. In earlier centuries it was unnecessary easy to find large, good quality specimens in the cliffs around the farmstead, but with increased tourism the cliffs have suffered, and now most of the stones have been removed from the surface of the rocks. Overzealous mineral collectors have played a large part there - magnificent zeolite samples from Teigarhorn can be found in many of the world's leading natural history museums. But erosion is a constant process, and new amygdales are revealed now and then, even though the process is very slow, as might be expected. It takes place along the shore when waves break away bits of cliff below the old farmstead. In 1975 Teigarhorn was finally protected as a natural monument and visitors are forbidden to remove stones from the area. Site wardens, however, are allowed to remove stones that fall from the cliffs along the shore.

The process which forms secondary minerals is different than that of primary minerals. Their formation process is therefore different from that of the primary minerals - these are the original minerals which formed when the magma solidified. Groundwater plays the key role in the formation of secondary minerals, and most of them contain water in their crystal structure. The alteration process occurs when cold or hot water flows through the porous and fractured rock, during which various chemicals

are dissolved from the rock. The groundwater takes these substances away, over longer or shorter distances, and new minerals form when the chemicals precipitate out of the water. Secondary minerals form either in vesicles (holes) in the rock, where they are called amygdales, or in cracks, where they are called veins.

Various sorts of secondary minerals are found in Iceland, and zeolites are relatively common. Zeolites are, however, special in some ways compared to other minerals in Iceland. They are usually classed in three groups, depending on their appearance, being fibrous, platy, or cubic in shape. Among the most common zeolites are chabazite, which is cubic, and scolecite, which is fibrous and usually has needle-like crystals radiating from one point. In Icelandic, zeolites are sometimes called geislasteinar, a name derived from the ray-like appearance of scolecite. Zeolites have a crystal framework made of silica and aluminium oxide, and the most common elements filling in the spaces are calcium, sodium and potassium. Although the chemical composition of the zeolites is fairly uniform, they are a varied group and of 50 types which occur naturally in the world, 20 can be found in Iceland. A closer look at the crystal structure reveals that it is very spacious and loose. This means that zeolites have a low density and fillers have easy access in and out of the framework. In this way, zeolites can take various substances out of their surroundings and into their crystal structure, and they are used a lot in industry and for pollution defences where they can absorb undesirable chemicals from the environment. In Icelandic the term "suðusteinn" is sometimes used, meaning boiling-stone – if zeolites are heated, they froth when the water is released from the framework. If zeolites that have been treated like this are placed in a humid environment, they reabsorb water.

The zeolites at Teigarhorn have a long history. The rock at Teigarhorn formed originally in volcanic eruptions 9–10 million years ago. Like elsewhere in the East Fjords, the rock is composed of many lavas that flowed over each other, coming from nearby volcanoes. In time the older layers of lava were buried beneath new ones, and in this way they reached a considerable depth. As the rocks became more deeply buried, the temperature of the groundwater flowing through them increased. Hydrothermal alteration increased with increasing temperature, and the lavas gradually became filled with amygdales and veins. First to form were low-temperature secondary minerals which form at or below 100°C. Zeolites, chabazite, and thomsonite are most common among these minerals. The deeper the rocks went, the greater the temperature, and different minerals formed which were stable at higher temperatures. They were zeolites such as scolecite, stilbite and epistilbite – these are all common at Teigarhorn, in addition to heulandite, which was first identified at Teigarhorn. So the rock at Teigarhorn first formed as lava at the surface, but it then went through several stages of alteration, until its spaces were almost completely filled by amygdales and veins, a few hundred metres below the surface. After glaciation began, the Ice Age glaciers scraped away the surface rock, and revealed the Teigarhorn rock.

Finally, it is worth reminding readers that geological formations like those at Teigarhorn are rare, and we are all obliged to treat them with respect and care. Unfortunately, many geological formations in this country have been badly treated, but with changing attitudes it is hoped that, in time, places like Teigarhorn will regain their former appearance, for which for which they originally became famous.

Jökulsárlón and Breiðamerkurjökull

Of all Iceland's natural wonders, Jökulsárlón is possibly the best known abroad. Many tourists come to Iceland with the principal aim of seeing the "Glacial Lagoon" with their own eyes, and no wonder because the lake and its surroundings are exquisite. At the same time, the history of this area is one of tremendous land changes, and because of thinning of the Vatnajökull icecap the appearance of the area has completely changed over the last hundred years. The lake called Jökulsárlón is one of Iceland´s youngest natural phenomena, and it first formed about 80 years ago. At that time, the Breiðamerkurjökull glacier extended much further across the coastal sand plain than it does now, and doubtless no one imagined how the landscape was going to change. What most concerns us now, however, is how much change will take place. If the current trend for global climate change continues, then Breiðamerkurjökull will eventually disappear as a result of warming, and Jökulsárlón will cut the coastline like a fjord.

Breiðamerkurjökull is one of the largest outlet glaciers flowing southwards from Vatnajökull, and the largest one east of Öræfajökull. Breiðamerkurjökull can be said to originate from either side of a relatively high mountain range in southern Vatnajökull, named Esjufjöll. In front of Breiðamerkurjökull is a fairly large sand plain called Breiðamerkursandur, created by glacial action in recent centuries. In front of the middle of Breiðamerkurjökull´s snout lies that pearl of nature, Jökulsárlón itself, which is the deepest lake in Iceland at 268 m deep. From it flows the river Jökulsá á Breiðamerkursandi - the shortest glacial river in the country, but also one of the most immense. The flowrate of Breiðamerkurjökull is about 500 m per year, and based on that figure, the ice takes an estimated 40-50 years to move down from the Esjufjöll mountains to the lake.

Breiðamerkurjökull's history is interwoven with that of Vatnajökull. At the end of the last glaciation, almost all of Iceland's glaciers vanished because the climate was

much warmer than it is now. About 2500 years ago, large icecaps had already formed because of a cooling climate, although the glaciers were still small compared to their current status. At the time of Iceland's settlement, the snout of Breiðamerkurjökull is thought to have been about 15-20 km further inland, and in front of the glacier there was probably a fairly fertile valley. In confirmation of this, a number of farmsteads in this area are named in old records. After about 1200, however, the climate in Iceland began to cool, and that caused the glaciers to advance. In the following centuries, Breiðamerkurjökull advanced steadily and destroyed farms and land. In about 1700, Breiðamörk was the last farm to be taken by the glacier. Only two farms remained on Breiðamerkursandur: Kvísker, which still stands above the main road between the rivers Kvíá and Fjallsá; and Fell, which stood easternmost on the sand plain and was abandoned in 1869 because of encroaching glacial rivers. Breiðamerkurjökull advanced even further, and was at its largest in about 1890 when its snout was only about a kilo-

metre from the coast. At this time, Jökulsá á Breiðamerkursandi flowed directly from the glacier to the sea, and it was frequently an obstacle to travel between the districts on either side of the sand plain. At its worst, the river was impassable for most of the year.

After 1890 the glacier began to retreat, and its snout gradually moved away from the coast. This was not a steady process, and the glacier actually advanced slightly in the 1920s. Since 1930, however, the glacier has retreated again, and in 1933-34 a lake began to form in front of the glacier. Such lakes form because the bases of outlet glaciers often lie lower than the surrounding ground, especially if they dig themselves down through thick layers of sediment. In the case of Breiðamerkurjökull, a large and powerful glacier, the base of the glacier is about 200-300 m lower than the adjacent land, and the glacier lies in a sort of deep chute that is far below sea level and extends tens of kilometres under the glacier, in towards the land. This means that if Breiðamerkurjökull were to vanish, a 25 kilo-

metre-long fjord would be formed, similar to Hvalfjörður, the fjord north of Reykjavík. In the 20th century Breiðamerkurjökull retreated about 5 km from its maximum point in about 1900.

Retreat of the glacier and the formation of Jökulsárlón have influenced the land between the glacier and the coast in many ways. When the river Jökulsá flowed directly from the glacier to the sea, it carried with it a considerable amount of glacial silt which was deposited on the coast, strengthening it. After Jökulsárlón formed, the deposits from the river largely ceased because the glacial silt settles in the lake itself rather than being carried by the river into the sea. This can be readily seen in aerial photographs of the southeast coast. After the sediment stopped being carried into the sea, it no longer balanced out the sea erosion, so the sea has encroached along the coast at Breiðamerkursandur. Measured coastal erosion has averaged about eight metres each year over the last decade, and the coastline has moved steadily closer to the lake. If things continue like this, then the land between the lake and the ocean will

disappear and Jökulsárlón will become a coastal fjord instead of a separate lake. This process is in fact well-advanced, since the sea floods into the lake at high tide, making it a saltwater lagoon. If this natural process is allowed to reach completion, it will have serious consequences for transport. In 1967 a bridge was erected over the river Jökulsá, on the strip of land between the lagoon and the sea, and if the land goes, so will the bridge. In recent years there has therefore been an emphasis on coastal defence construction at the mouth of the Jökulsá, to prevent any further erosion..

Jökulsárlón is not the only feature worth looking at on Breiðamerkursandur. At the western edge of the glacier is Breiðárlón, a glacial lake about half the size of Jökulsárlón. The river Breiðá flows from Breiðárlón into Fjallsárlón, another glacial lake in front of Fjallsjökull. If the topography of the base of Breiðamerkurjökull is studied, it can be seen that Breiðárlón lies in a much smaller and shallower depression than Jökulsárlón does. It can also be seen that another small lake will probably form, given time, between Breiðárlón and

Jökulsárlón. In fact almost all the outlet glaciers southeast of the Vatnajökull ice-cap have dug themselves down into the soft substrate, and with the retreat of the glaciers, small lakes like Breiðárlón and Fjallsárlón will form in front of most glacier snouts in this area. At about the same time as Jökulsárlón formed, there was another glacial lake in front of the eastern part of Breiðamerkurjökull. It was called Stemmulón, and a fairly large glacial river, called Stemma, flowed from it. Stemma was short lived, and in 1990 it vanished from its course. It suddenly began to flow alongside Breiðamerkurjökull, over into Jökulsárlón, and left its old, dried-up bed behind. Now Stemmulón is beautiful and clear, lying among moraines, less than a kilometre's walk from the main road.

Standing at Jökulsárlón, the icebergs on the lake are first to catch the eye. They float around the lagoon and can be enormous. Only about ten percent of each iceberg is above the lagoon's surface, so care must be taken when sailing on the lagoon. Looking up at Breiðamerkurjökull, the medial moraines are clearly visible. Moraines form on the edges of glaciers when they slide past nunataks - rocky peaks sticking out of the ice. The glacier erodes the sides of the nunatak and carries the rock fragments away, down to the snout of the glacier. When the ice-streams of the outlet glacier unite below the nunatak, the rock fragments collect together in a single stripe, which continues unbroken all the way down the glacier. The medial moraines on Breiðamerkurjökull form where the glacier slides past Esjufjöll and Mávabyggðir, so usually people talk about Esjufjallarönd which is farthest east on the glacier, and also the largest of the stripes. But Mávabyggðarönd lies further west, and it can easily be followed with a bare eye up to the nunataks at Mávabyggðir.

Finally, it is worth mentioning that Jökulsárlón has been used as the setting for some well-known Hollywood movies. These include two James Bond films, A View to a Kill and Die Another Day. In the latter, a tremendous car chase takes place on the frozen lake, but normally Jökulsárlón is never frozen because seawater floods into it. When filming took place, the lake was dammed, causing the lake's denser saltwater to sink to the bottom, allowing the freshwater at the surface to freeze.

Öræfajökull

The fourth of August is a black day in the minds of many Icelanders. That day in 2005, Halldór Ásgrímsson, prime minister of Iceland, announced the new altitude measurement for Iceland´s highest peak, Hvannadalshnúkur. The mountain was first measured precisely in the summer of 1904, by Danish surveyors, and they thought that it was 2119 m high. This was the official altitude of Hvannadalshnúkur for the next century – until the fateful day arrived. Then it was measured at 2109.6 m, although it is debateable if all Icelanders accept that result. Despite this, Öræfajökull still holds the title of the highest and greatest volcano in the country. In fact, the volcano is not only big by Icelandic standards, with a volume of about 350-400 km³, it is among the largest volcanoes in Europe. But what lies behind these numbers? Why is Öræfajökull such a big and powerful volcano?

Öræfajökull is a central volcano – a name given to volcanoes that erupt repeatedly in one place, producing both acid and basic magma. In this way the volcano is built up gradually, and in the case of Öræfajökull a large stratovolcano has developed. On its summit is a 500 m deep caldera, full of glacial ice. The oldest lavas that can be traced to Öræfajökull are 700,000-800,000 years old. They can be examined at the foot of the mountain Svínafellsfjall, behind the farm Svínafell. Öræfajökull is considered one of the oldest active central volcanoes in Iceland. Two eruptions have occurred in Öræfajökull since Iceland was settled: in 1362 and 1727. The latter eruption was fairly large, but the former was one of the largest and most powerful explosive eruptions to occur in Iceland in the last thousand years. About 10 km³ of eruptive material was ejected from the volcano, and ash from the eruption was found widely in Europe. The farming area below the glacier, which was previously well-vegetated and called Litla-Hérað, was almost completely destroyed, and the area

instantly became a desert of pumice. The area below the glacier remained uninhabited for several decades, and from that time on it was known as Öræfi, or Wasteland. Volcanologist Sigurður Þórarinsson wrote one of the first comprehensive works about Öræfajökull in the mid 20th century, and he discussed the 1362 eruption in detail.

Öræfajökull is in some ways different to many of Iceland's other central volcanoes. For one thing, it is not situated on a rift zone; instead it is on some sort of volcanic flank zone, east of the main volcanic belt. Material erupted from volcanoes on these flank zones has a different chemical composition than most other volcanoes. The concentrations of alkali-metals sodium and potassium are higher there, so they are called alkaline volcanoes. Furthermore, there is no visible fissure swarm at Öræfajökull. The unusual position of the volcano on a flank zone also means that it built up on much older crust, and this crust provides a solid foundation for the Öræfajökull volcano. The dense crust, along with the constraints of the Ice Age glaciers, has allowed the volcano to build up to its present size. Next to the summit crater is the highest point, Hvannadalshnúkur. It is composed of acid rock, rhyolite,

and was formed in an eruption when thick, highly viscous magma pushed its way out of a crater on the caldera rim.

The Öræfajökull volcano is extremely hazardous because it is close to inhabited areas. Its eruptions are explosive, and because they occur beneath a glacier, glacial floods (jökulhlaup) pour down the mountainside during the eruptions. The greatest risk undoubtedly comes from pyroclastic surges – which are common in acid eruptions. A pyroclastic surge happens in an explosive eruption when part of the eruption column collapses to the ground and flows down the sides of the volcano. The surge contains a fairly low proportion of ash, but it is correspondingly gas-rich and low density, so it flows at great speed over the ground. Such pyroclastic surges are extremely hot and pull oxygen out of the atmosphere, so all living things in their path suffocate. It has been suggested that, in the 1362 eruption, a pyroclastic surge like this destroyed all life in the area around the glacier, up to 200–300 people perhaps, in the blink of an eye. With this in mind, it is best to be wary of the volcano, and it is carefully monitored by scientists and the Department of Civil Protection.

South

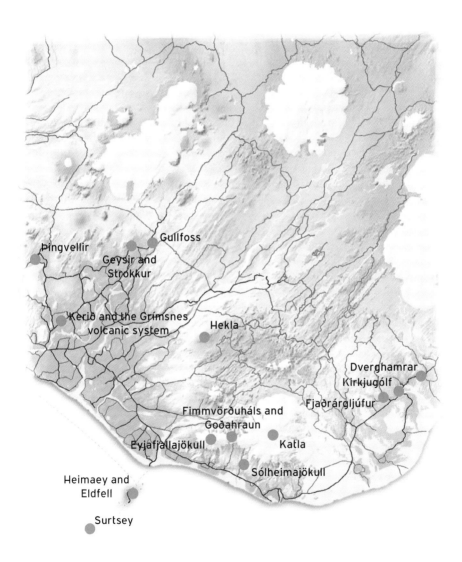

Þingvellir

Gullfoss

Geysir and Strokkur

Kerið and the Grímsnes volcanic system

Hekla

Dverghamrar
Kirkjugólf

Fjaðrárgljúfur

Fimmvörðuháls and Goðahraun

Eyjafjallajökull

Katla

Sólheimajökull

Heimaey and Eldfell

Surtsey

Dverghamrar and Kirkjugólf

Dverghamrar and Kirkjugólf are two distinctive columnar jointed formations at Síða, just east of Kirkjubæjarklaustur. They were formed in similar ways, but the outcomes are quite different. Kirkjugólf is a surface formed from columnar jointed basalt, and the ends of the columns point upwards. At a later date, glacial ice and ocean waves have smoothed and polished the surface. The Dverghamrar formation is also made of columnar jointed basalt, but in contrast to Kirkjugólf, it is the sides of the columns that are seen. The names for these formations suggest old ideas about their origins and uses. Kirkjugólf (Church Floor) was obviously thought to be so uniform looking that the only plausible explanation was that it had been hewn and laid by humans. The name Dverghamrar (Dwarf Rocks), on the other hand, points towards Icelandic folklore, although no tales connected to the place name have been found. It is, however, easy to discern outlines of doors and buildings belonging to the dwarves in the assorted cliffs. But modern folk are hard-

ly prepared to accept such tales of origin, so the question remains – how did these beautiful columnar jointed formations come to be?

First, a "runny" basalt lava needs to be dammed and form a deep, wide lava pond. If the pond does not drain away, the lava just solidifies and creates a thick layer of basalt lava. Basaltic magma solidifies fully at about 1000°C, and after that the lava cools gradually down to ambient temperature. On cooling, the lava naturally shrinks, and this contraction creates tension in the rock. Eventually the rock gives way and cracks, so cooling fractures are formed on its surface – this seems to first happen when the lava's temperature is about 900°C. As the layer of lava cools internally, the fractures deepen towards the hot centre, and the lava cracks internally. Cooling fractures always lie at right angles to the cooling surface of the lava, which is usually its surface, but can often be its undersurface too.

The splitting of the lava creates prisms or columns of rock, which are often six-sid-

ed. In forming hexagonal cross-sections, the columns acquire a maximum surface area relative to the length of the cooling fractures between them, so this is the optimal shape. Formation of regular lava columns is not, however, a straightforward process, and this may be readily seen because even the most regular columnar jointed formations have a few columns that are not hexagonal. At Kirkjugólf, for example, columns with four and up to seven sides can be seen, and the reader may even find a triangular column here and there.

The columns at Dverghamrar and Kirkjugólf were initially formed by the solidification and cooling of thick horizontal lavas. The age of these formations is not well known, but the bedrock in the area is about 1-2 million years old, and the lavas are probably the same age. In the upper part of Dverghamrar is what is called an entablature – smaller, irregular columns which point in all directions. An entablature forms when cooling is more rapid than that of normal columnar basalt. It is often seen as a sign that water

has had access to the lava and suddenly chilled it. Since the formation of the lavas, glaciers have advanced over them and eroded them. At the end of the last glaciation, the sea level was higher for a while, and Dverghamrar stood out in the ocean, but Kirkjugólf was part of a shallow sea bed that now forms the surrounding lowlands. Wave action has thus further shaped the area, especially at Dverghamrar.

Dverghamrar and Kirkjugólf are among the most beautiful and charming locations for columnar jointed basalt in Iceland. Other places worth mentioning are Svartifoss at Skaftafell, Kálfshamarsvík on the Skagi peninsula, Gerðuberg on Snæfellsnes and Aldeyjarfoss on the river Skjálfandafljót. The influence of these places is present in architecture, and Icelandic architects have been diligent in using the columnar form for inspiration. When it comes to design, however, the architects can hardly match the forces of nature, and everyone who visits the visits these areas ought to be convinced of this.

Fjaðrárgljúfur

Fjaðrárgljúfur is one of the best-kept secrets of Icelandic nature. Because of its position, it is not easily seen from a distance, so it is hidden from most travellers even though it is well worth their attention. Fjaðrárgljúfur is about 1.5 km long and around 100 m deep at its greatest depth. Few canyons are as magnificent and yet at the same time so accessible. The canyon walls are mainly composed of móberg (hyaloclastite), and have been carved into spectacular cliffs, with rock pillars and promontories in many places along the canyon edges. Below the mouth of the canyon, where the innocent-looking Fjaðrá flows into the river Skaftá, the seemingly endless expanse of the Skaftáreldahraun lava can be seen. The entire surroundings have a profound effect on the visitor, but may provoke a difficult question too. How did this canyon form? The small Fjaðrá river which winds along the canyon bottom is an unlikely cause – judging by its present appearance, at least. To discover the truth we need to look further back in time, all the way to the end of

the last glaciation in fact, about 10,000 years ago. If readers want to solve the puzzle for themselves, then they are advised to stop at the end of this paragraph and walk instead up the canyon, all the way to the uppermost waterfalls on the river Fjaðrá. Just upstream of the falls is a clue that could give an attentive visitor enough information to decipher how the canyon formed. Note in particular the height difference in the landscape – it is the key to the puzzle.

At the end of the last glaciation, when the glaciers were retreating and the lowlands were ice free, a voluminous and sediment-rich glacial river flowed from beneath the edge of the glacier for a time, where Fjaðrárgljúfur is now. The glacial river was much more powerful than the current river, so it was much more erosive. Where Fjaðrárgljúfur is now, the glacial river encountered resistance in the shape of a rock barrier, a sort of natural dam, and a small glacial lake formed above the blockage. However, the height difference between the lake and

the lowland below was considerable, so the river began at once to erode down into the móberg bedrock and carve out the canyon. While the river was at work down there, a constant supply of gravel and sand was delivered into the glacial lake above, and it was soon filled by river sediment. In this situation, gravel terraces usually form in the lake, with their flat tops marking where the lake surface was when they formed. In the valley above Fjaðrárgljúfur, gravel terraces can indeed be seen, but they are at various heights, with the highest furthest up the valley and their flat tops becoming lower nearer to the river's course. What happened was that after the glacial lake was filled by sediment, the glacial river gradually eroded the rock barrier which originally dammed the valley. When this happened, the river's erosion surface was lowered, and it began to erode down through the sediments in the old glacial lake. The gravel terraces now seen at the highest point on either side of the river valley, therefore indicate the original surface of the glacial lake, but

the terraces closer to the coast mark the river's erosion surface at different stages. The river's current erosion surface is at the same elevation as the brink of the highest waterfall above the canyon, and the river is still eroding downwards although it does so more slowly than when it was a powerful glacial river.

Visitors can choose between enjoying the canyon from above or below. Most prefer to walk up the path along the eastern edge of the canyon, where the view is best. Great care must be taken along the canyon edge because it is a big drop to the canyon floor, and the future for anyone falling off the edge is hardly in dispute. If people choose the other route, along the canyon floor, they can expect to wade across the river several times as it winds gently between the cliff walls on either side. The water is not deep though, and the trip into the canyon is amazing, so few people should feel cheated in their choice of route.

Katla

There are few things geologists enjoy more than discussing Katla, the volcano beneath Mýrdalsjökull. Over the years much has been written about earthquake activity and a possible eruption under the Mýrdalsjökull icecap, signs of geothermal activity in Katla's caldera, and whether Katla is poised to erupt. If a geologist is lucky enough to meet people who are keen on geology and foolish enough to ask about Katla, the audience may not easily escape. The curious will get a lecture about what has happened beneath the glacier over recent decades, with brief digressions on possible connections to eruptions in Eyjafjallajökull, ancient explosive eruptions, Kötluhlaup (glacial outburst floods), and other interesting things. It might be wise to stop the geologist at once in this situation, or else the lecture may run on and on. On further discussion, it is obvious that people have their own ideas about Katla, and opinions are divided on all these topics. This leaves one question, is it possible to predict when Katla will next erupt? Because Katla is so

dangerous, it is important to try to collect as much data as possible to answer this question. There is in fact only one sure answer – with every passing day, the next eruption comes one day closer.

Katla is the central volcano in the middle of a large volcanic system. The Katla volcanic system extends over the whole of the Mýrdalsjökull icecap, and its fissure system stretches tens of kilometres north towards Vatnajökull. The Eldgjá fissure which erupted early in the 10th century is thought to be part of this system, but apart from this, most of the activity has occurred under or near Mýrdalsjökull. Eruptions in Katla are mentioned in historical records from the 13th century. Over 20 layers of ash have been identified from eruptions in the Katla system in the period since Iceland was settled, so Katla has erupted twice each century, on average. The last big eruption was in 1918, and it is now almost a hundred years since "she" was last heard from properly. However, it

is possible that up to three small eruptions occurred beneath the glacier – in 1955, 1999 and 2011 – but none of them made it through the icecap. Since the end of the last glaciation, Katla has erupted at least 300 times, so it is one of the most active volcanoes in the country.

Geologists began to study Katla in the early part of last century, and since then, attempts have been made to map the topography of the ground below the icecap, with the assistance of radio-echo sounding equipment. In 1970 an enormous caldera below the centre of the icecap was discovered during this research. At the end of the 20th century an accurate survey was made, and it revealed a large caldera, up to 600-700 m deep and about ten kilometres in diameter. The caldera is full of ice and undoubtedly formed during cataclysmic eruptions in the Katla volcanic system, but it is unclear when they occurred. Research on tephra (ash and larger particles) from Katla has shown that there have been several huge explosive eruptions, most recently about 12,000 years ago. The rim of the caldera is generally about 1200-1400 m above sea level, and the floor of the caldera is at about 650-800 m. The southern portion of the caldera floor sits higher than the northern part, and there are signs of considerable volcanic activity on long ridges that rise a few hundred metres above the caldera floor. The caldera rim is cut by a few deep gaps where large outlet glaciers now flow down to the lowland. The lowest gap is on the eastern side of the caldera, where Kötlujökull flows out to Mýrdalssandur, but there is also a deep gap by Sólheimajökull in the south, Entujökull in the north, and Sandfellsjökull to the northeast.

Katla is often considered the most alarming of Icelandic volcanoes, for several reasons. Firstly, Katla is close to human habitation, standing guard over the Mýrdalur region and the farmland east of Mýrdalssandur. People in these areas will be severely affected when Katla erupts, and eruptions happen frequently. The main point though, is that Katla is covered by a

thick glacier. Consequently, an eruption in Katla is most frequently a very explosive eruption (Plinian), in which the subglacial eruption produces enormous ash falls and glacial outburst floods (jökulhlaup). Most dangerous are the terrible floods that break out from beneath the glacier following the volcanic activity. They occur when magma, discharged in the eruption, melts the glacier rapidly. Since the ice is a few hundred metres thick in the caldera, a large portion of the eruption's early energy is used in melting the ice. Despite the ice's thickness, it usually only takes the eruption a few hours to melt its way through the glacier, which says a lot about the power of a Katla eruption.

Contemporary reports of eruptions indicate that there is not much warning before a Katla eruption. Earthquakes are only felt in the Mýrdalur region a few hours before an eruption; although with the modern sensitive earthquake monitoring system it should be possible to recognise the prelude earlier. At the beginning of the eruption a lot of meltwater is produced, which runs almost instantly down the mountainside and soon bursts out from beneath Mýrdalsjökull's outlet glaciers. These floods are called Kötluhlaup, glacial outburst floods from Katla, and they always accompany an eruption from Katla. Eyewitness descriptions of previous eruptions indicate that the floodwater bursts out immediately after the eruption cloud over Katla is first noticed, and sometimes even before the eruption cloud is seen. Since settlement times, most Kötluhlaup have come from beneath Kötlujökull, on to Mýrdalssandur, but on three occasions they have come from Sólheimajökull. About 1600 years ago, 500 years before people settled in Iceland, Kötluhlaup burst out from under Entujökull and flooded down the Markarfljót river channel, out over the Landeyjar area. There are thus three possible main flood paths, and at the start of the eruption it is almost impossible to say where the flood will occur, although Mýrdalssandur is the most common flood path.

Kötluhlaup floods are among the most regular disasters to happen on Earth. Every Katla eruption is accompanied by a number of floods while the eruption lasts, but the first flood is usually the largest by far. They include so much ice and tephra that the flood water is often more like a mudflow than a flood of water, and the leading edge of the flood can be many metres high. Katla eruptions vary in size, but the 1755 and 1918 eruptions were among the largest eruptions from the volcano since Iceland was settled. Such eruptions are followed by terrible floods, and it is thought that in the 1755 and 1918 Kötluhlaup the maximum flow rate reached 300,000 m³/s. By comparison, the maximum flow rate of the Skeiðará outburst flood in 1996 was about 50,000–60,000 m³/s, and the average flow rate of the Amazon at its estuary is thought to be about 200,000 m³/s. Because of the amount of tephra in the flood water its density is much greater than usual, so it can easily carry along large rocks and icebergs. This was demonstrated well in the flood of 1918 – the photographs of towering icebergs in the flood are incredible. A large móberg (hyaloclastite) rock was also washed onto the sand, about 15 km away from Kötlujökull. This rock has been named Kötluklettur (Katla's Rock) and its weight has been estimated at about 1400 tons.

The Kötluhlaup floods are not the only danger that accompanies a Katla eruption though, as the eruption column itself is also dangerous. In the 1918 eruption, the column rose 14 km into the air on the first day, and ash fell 30 km away from the volcano in the first hour after the eruption broke through the ice. The eruption column is accompanied by a risk of lightning, and lightning can be expected up to 40 km away from Katla. In the 1755 eruption, two people died after being hit by lightning from the eruption column.

Although the Kötluhlaup floods are very dangerous, they do not only bring ruin and destruction. A large portion of the sediment carried by the floodwaters is deposited on the pre-existing expanse of sand, thickening it, and a lot of mud is carried into the sea. When the first people settled in Iceland there was a fairly large inlet, Kerlingafjörður, in the coastline west of Hjörleifshöfði. It was gradually filled in by floods from Katla and had probably vanished by the 14th century. In the 1918 eruption, Kötlutangi, the southernmost part of Mýrdalssandur, extended seawards by about three kilometres as a result of sediment transfer. A lot of the sediment from Kötluhlaup floods is carried by ocean currents along the coastline, building up the coast. The coast at Vík in Mýrdalur migrated seawards in this way until 1970, but then the process was reversed, and the sea began to break the coast away again. Since then, waves have eroded about 350 m of coastline below the town, so the town is threatened, and a breakwater was built out from the coast in 2011 to reduce erosion. Even though models suggest that the next Kötluhlaup could cause a tidal wave to strike low-lying areas at Vík, the sediment from the flood would no doubt move the coastline much further out and counter balance the coastal erosion. This shows clearly how the forces of nature work in an endless cycle of creation and destruction.

Dyrhólaey

Dyrhólaey is an extremely popular spot with tourists, particularly because of the varied birdlife there, but the landscape and the view from the headland also attract people. Dyrhólaey was declared a protected site in 1978 because of the rich birdlife, and for this reason access to the headland has been restricted during breeding season. Icelanders divide Dyrhólaey in two parts, Háey (High Island) in the west and Láey (Low Island) in the east, and there is a short road on to both parts. In fact, Dyrhólaey is not an island at all because it is attached to the mainland and has been the country's southern outpost for most of Iceland's history. Its position changed, however, about 100 years ago when the 1918 Kötluhlaup carried a large quantity of sediment down Mýrdalssandur, east of Vík í Mýrdal, and moved the coastline southwards a few kilometres. The headland of sand that formed was named Kötlutangi and it extends further south than Dyrhólaey. Ocean waves have been diligent about scraping Kötlutangi, and have shortened it by around ten metres a year, although it will be a few more years until Dyrhólaey is once more the southernmost point in the country. That seems unavoidable unless Katla sends another delivery down Mýrdalssandur and moves the coastline out again.

Unlike Kötlutangi, Dyrhólaey is fairly old, formed originally as a móberg (hyaloclastite) island in a submarine eruption similar to the one that created Surtsey. Strangely little has been written about the geology of the headland, but a local farmer, Einar Einarsson from Skammadalshóll, has studied Dyrhólaey more than most people and has collected information about the geology. He described the formation of Dyrhólaey in an article in 1968, and his observations have mostly stood the test of time, although no one has done any further geological research as of yet. Einar thought that the island was formed in at least two separate eruptions. The first eruption was along a fissure where the eastern end of Dyrhólaey is now, called Skorpunef. There are beautiful columnar jointed formations down on the beach, and further out are sea stacks, called Stampur and Sker. These are remains of the same eruptive fissure, but the sea has eroded away the outer part of the crater remnants. In the western part of Dyrhólaey is another eruptive fissure, which has mostly been eroded away. Einar thought that the majority of the current "island" was formed in an eruption from that fissure. The northernmost crater remnants are at Hildardrangur, the rock by the northwest corner of Dyrhólaey, and about 600‒700 metres south of Háey is Mávadrangur, the southernmost part of the fissure. The eruption began as a submarine eruption with a lot of explosive activity and tephra production, which

built up a large heap of ash and rock fragments initially. At some point in time the sea stopped being able to get into the magma conduit, and the eruption changed to a calm lava eruption, similar to that of the Surtsey eruption. After that, lava ran down from the tephra mound and formed a fairly thick lava flow down on the beach that the sea waves had already created around the newly formed island. These two chapters in the eruption can be readily seen in the different rocks on Dyrhólaey – Háey is nearly entirely made of móberg (hyaloclastite), while Lágey is comprised of lavas. The division between them can be seen above the beach Kirkjufjara, in the middle of Dyrhólaey's southern cliffs, and there it is easy to see how the lava has flowed from Háey, downhill to the beach. Einar thought that Dyrhólaey had formed in an interglacial period when the sea level was similar to now, but that after its formation, glaciers had advanced over it and eroded it. This means that Dyrhólaey probably formed some time before the last glaciation was at its maximum level about 25,000 years ago, but apart from this it is difficult to say how old it is.

Ever since the formation of Dyrhólaey, glacial and oceanic advances have shaped it at their whim. The southernmost point is called Tóin, and in it is the famous archway or "door" for which Dyrhólaey is famous. The archway is not very large, although boats can easily pass through it. The archway in Dyrhólaey is a good example of the power of erosion and the varied forms that ocean waves carve in the country's cliffs. Because of the position of Dyrhólaey, the ocean waves have worked on it from the start, both from the southwest and southeast, and created a narrow headland projecting to the south. The sea's waves have worked ceaselessly on the rocks, and over time they have cut into weaknesses in the rock so that sea caves formed on both sides

of the headland. Eventually the caves combined, and a hole formed through the headland – now seen as Dyrhólagat.

From the start, the "island" has been growing smaller, and Einar from Skammadalshóll estimated that hardly more than a quarter of the original Dyrhólaey is left. Certainly it takes a long time to break down a whole island of móberg, at least in human terms, but the erosion there is so organic that we see it happening literally before our eyes. In May 2012, a section four to five metres wide and 100 metres long fell down onto the beach on Lágey. The cliffs where the rock fall happened are about 20-30 m high, so quite a large volume fell there. Unfortunately, at the same time as the rock fall happened, two tourists were walking along the edge of the cliff, on a hiking trail. They went down with the rock fall, but in some miraculous manner they stayed all the time on rock at the top of the scree. So they were not buried in the debris and escaped with relatively minor injuries, broken bones and bruises. In 2015 there were two more large rock falls along the cliffs of Dyrhólaey.

It is of course erosion by the sea that causes the rock falls on Dyrhólaey – the ocean waves are nowhere close to being finished with it. They will continue to erode the land and the archway until the inevitable happens and the roof of Dyhólagat gives way. After that, Tóin will be left as a sea stack off the coast of Dyrhólaey, not unlike the Reynisdrangir stacks in front of Mt. Reynisfjall now. Judging by the thickness of the roof over Dyrhólagat, it will probably be a long time until this happens, and even when it does, visitors of the future need not despair. If the large arch collapses, there is another smaller one, sometimes called Grynnragat, further in on Tóin, and that would take over the role of the other as one of the main attractions of Dyhólaey, so we will be able to enjoy Dyhólaey well into the future.

Sólheimajökull

Sólheimajökull has long been the subject of research for glaciologists who have studied it from various angles. The extent of the glaciers in earlier times can tell us much about climate and climatic changes through the centuries, but the glacial history of Sólheimajökull is in many ways unusual compared to that of other Icelandic glaciers. Ridges of old moraine (rock debris from the glacier) are found widely in the vicinity of the glacier, both immediately in front of the glacier's snout and also further forward on the Sólheimasandur plain. But there are also beautifully shaped and tightly interlaced moraine ridges up at Hrossatungur on the southwest side of the glacier. These ridges, called terminal moraines, show where the snout of the glacier used to be, but their age fits poorly with the ages of other terminal moraines elsewhere in the country. Geologists believe that Iceland's glaciers had more or less disappeared at the end of the last glaciation, around 9000-11,000 years ago.

The Ice Age glaciers left behind large and conspicuous terminal moraines in many places around the country. For the first thousand years after the end of glaciation, Iceland was almost glacier-free, but new glaciers gradually began to grow because of a cooling climate. The present glaciers are therefore not the remains of Ice Age glaciers; rather they are for the most part formed in the last few thousand years. The glaciers have probably grown a lot since settlement times, and at the end of the 19th century Icelandic glaciers were at their largest since the end of glaciation.

About a hundred years ago, Sólheimajökull extended quite a lot further than where the current main car park is by the glacier. In front of it is a low hill, Jökulhaus, and around 1900 it was almost covered by glacial ice. This says a lot about the thickness of the glacier at that time and how much it has thinned, because Jökulhaus now towers over 100 m above its surround-

ings. Unlike most other Icelandic glaciers, the period around 1900 does not mark Sól-heimajökull's maximum extent since the end of glaciation. The aforementioned moraines are actually much older than the end of the 19th century. On the way to Sólheimajökull from the main ring road, ancient moraines are widely visible in the landscape, and they are arranged in long ridges at right-angles to the road. Where the ring road crosses the Sólheimasandur plain, there are even older moraines; these have been dated, and the oldest ones appear to be a few thousand years old, with younger moraines lined up behind the oldest ones.

Judging by this, Sólheimajökull used to extend a few kilometres further out onto the sand plain than it did at the end of the 19th century, which is very unusual. Several theories have been put forward to explain this discrepancy – the main one being that the collection area for Sólheimajökull, up on the Mýrdalsjökull icecap, used to be much

larger; so a larger ice-mass was carried down by the glacier, but the collection area has since shrunk due to climate change, volcanic activity or geothermal activity beneath the ice. A second explanation could be that the glacier used to be in equilibrium with Iceland's climate, but in recent centuries it has simply been unable to re-establish that equilibrium. It should, by rights, have reached much further out onto the sand plain at the end of the 19th century. If this explanation is correct then eruptions in Katla may have been part of the cause because the largest eruption melted about 10% or more of the Mýrdalsjökull icecap. A loss of such a volume of ice high up on the icecap could have had a detrimental effect on the icecap's outlet glaciers and reduced their advancement. However, these events are unclear, and Sólheimajökull's previous size still requires an acceptable explanation.

Sólheimajökull's 20th-century history is, on the other hand, well known, and regular measurements of the snout's position began in 1930. The glacier seems to have reacted sharply to climatic changes in the last decades. From its maximum extent at the start of the 20th century, the snout has retreated by almost two kilometres because of the warming climate, and this has happened in two main steps. Until after the mid 20th century the glacier retreated steadily, but between 1970 and 1995 the snout advanced about 500 m. This advance was related to a slightly cooling climate from the middle of the century until 1980 and increased precipitation on Mýrdalsjökull. 1995 was the last year during which the glacier advanced, and the snout was then in a location similar to where it was in the 1940s, with some way to go to reach as far as it did at the start of the century.

After 1995, however, you could say that the "economy" of Sólheimajökull collapsed, losing more mass than it gained, and the glacier has been retreating faster than ever. It took the glacier only about twelve years to retreat to where it was in 1970. Between 1995 and 2013, the glacier retreated by about 900 m, or around 50 m a year on average, with a maximum of 134 m in 2008. Readers can best appreciate these changes when they arrive at Sólheimajökull – the glacier's snout reached to the car park in 1995, where the café now stands. In the spring of 2008 a glacial lake began to form in front of the snout; it is expanding rapidly and probably further accelerates the retreat of the glacier. This development is unlikely to stop in the near future – long sections of Sólheimajökull's base lie lower than the ground in front of the snout, so a long and fairly deep lake will be left behind in the valley when Sólheimajökull eventually retreats to the edge of the Mýrdalsjökull icecap. The glacier's retreat makes it harder for tourists to visit the glacier because it is necessary to walk further from the road to reach the snout, and conditions also become

more dangerous at the retreating snout. This became evident in August 2014, when Sólheimajökull's snout was declared a danger zone. The glacier tongue that extended into the lake had lifted up and large icebergs had broken off it.

Over the centuries though, the glacier has been of little danger compared to the river which pours from beneath it. Jökulsá á Sólheimasandi has always been treacherous, good crossing points sadly lacking, and floods frequent because of glacial outbursts (jökulhlaup). The river has claimed many lives over the years, more than most other rivers in the country, it is said. From earliest times the river Jökulsá has also been called by the unusual name Fúlilækur, or Smelly Stream, referring to the sulphurous stench that comes from it. The sulphur smell points to geothermal water issuing from beneath Sólheimajökull, into the river, and ice cauldrons in the Mýrdalsjökull icecap show where geothermal activity hides beneath the ice. The geothermal activity is connected to the great volcano Katla, which lies beneath Mýrdalsjökull. The icecap obscures the volcano's large caldera, and Sólheimajökull flows through a gap in its southern rim. Consequently, Sólheimajökull is one of Katla's flood paths, and if an eruption occurs in southwest Mýrdalsjökull there is a risk of an outburst flood down Jökulsá á Sólheimasandi. In the last thousand years many floods have taken this route, and the sand plains of Sólheimasandur and Skógasandur were formed by large outburst floods before Iceland's settlement. After the settlement period only a few outburst floods from Katla have gone down Jökulsá á Sólheimasandi, while most have flowed out onto Mýrdalssandur. Landnáma, the Book of Settlements, tells of floods on Sólheimasandur which match surprisingly well with indications that a flood occurred on the sand plain around that time, probably in the 8th or 9th century. It is also thought that

an outburst flood occurred at the same time as an eruption in Katla in 920, or along with the Eldgjá eruption in 934. Since then Katla has spared Sólheimasandur, with the exception of the 1860 Katla eruption when part of the meltwater flowed down onto Sólheimasandur. It is also probable that the flood in Jökulsá á Sólheimasandi in the summer of 1999 was caused by a small subglacial eruption that did not manage to reach the surface of the glacier. Judging by the number of eruptions and the previous locations of eruptions within the Katla caldera, it is thought unlikely that the next outburst flood from Katla will come down Sólheimajökull.

Sólheimajökull is a pretty amazing place to visit, not least because the abrupt changes there remind us of the ongoing climate changes. The glacier used to be easily visible from the main road, but now it has almost disappeared in the valley behind Jökulhaus. For those who want to see the changes that have happened in the glacier, the film Chasing Ice is unreservedly recommended

– Sólheimajökull had a big role in it. However, travellers who go onto the glacier will not only be captivated by Sólheimajökull's surroundings and the changes in them, but also by the landscape of the glacier itself. Deep crevasses can be seen, glittering in the beautiful blue ice; the blue colour appears when sunlight passes through glacial ice which has been compressed deep within the glacier. During compression of the ice, air bubbles are removed from it and the ice crystals grow; large ice crystals and dense glacial ice absorb red light more than blue light, so the ice acquires a blue tinge. On top of the glacier are impressively tall heaps of sand called dirt cones, which often catch the traveller's eye. Sand and ash originally collects in glacial crevasses, but when spring arrives and the ice begins to melt in the summer heat, the sand insulates the underlying ice which melts less than the surrounding ice. The dirt cones remain, like some sort of inverted crevasse.

Fimmvörðuháls and Goðahraun

Fimmvörðuháls is the name of the big mountain ridge connecting Eyjafjallajökull, in the west, to Mýrdalsjökull in the east. Fimmvörðuháls has long been familiar to many people because one of Iceland's popular hiking trails, between the Þórsmörk area and Skógar, goes along the ridge, a kind of continuation of the Laugavegur hiking trail. Pioneers of mountain climbing in Iceland raised a mountain hut on Fimmvörðuháls in the early 1940s, and there are now two huts in use on the trail. The route is popular because of its amazing views, despite a well-known tendency to be foggy and difficult to navigate. On fine days the highlands to the north are in full view, Þórsmörk, Tindfjöll, and Fjallabak; and to the south is the limitless Atlantic Ocean. In fact, Antarctica lies 15,000 km directly south past the western tip of Africa, although the curvature of the earth prevents hikers from seeing so far. It could be said that a new chapter in the area's history began in 2010 when an eruption started on the north side of Fimmvörðuháls.

Lava from the eruption flowed over the hiking trail, and a new path had to be marked after the eruption ended. The popularity of the trail subsequently reached new heights, and the area is a paradise for geology enthusiasts.

Fimmvörðuháls lies between two unequally active central volcanoes, Eyjafjallajökull and Katla in Mýrdalsjökull. Katla has erupted a total of 21 times since the settlement, and it has been the most effusive of Iceland's central volcanoes, as measured in volume of volcanic material. In contrast, Eyjafjallajökull is generally a quiet volcano, although it is certainly a large one. From settlement times until the 21st century, only three eruptions have been known in Eyjafjallajökull, all fairly small. Nevertheless, the volcano beneath the Eyjafjallajökull glacier has managed to grow into a large stratovolcano, and it could be said that Fimmvörðuháls is really the eastern side of this. Consequently, on the ridge there are old volcanoes associated with the Eyja-

fjallajökull central volcano, both móberg (hyaloclastite) ridges erupted beneath glaciers, and younger lava erupted after the Ice Age glaciers melted. Most of these eruptions were along fissures with an east-west trend, similar to the long axis of the Eyjafjallajökull stratovolcano. This trend is evident in the landscape when walking onto the ridge from Skógar, and ridges, fissures, and faults can be seen at right angles to the hiking trail.

The highest part of Fimmvörðuháls was best known for its view, which was quickly spoiled in fog and bad weather. When that happened, most people were anxious to get off the ridge as soon as possible. This changed in March 2010 when an eruption began, rather unexpectedly, on the northern side of the ridge. The prelude to the eruption was actually long, because in 1992 a series of earthquakes began beneath Eyjafjallajökull. This seismic activity culminated in a magmatic intrusion in 1994, and magma was again intruded up under the Eyjafjallajökull volcano in 1999, but then there was break in activity until the end of 2009. A strong series of earthquakes began then, at the same time as magma was

intruded – this time at a higher level than before. Sometime before the eruption, magma had arrived below the eastern part of the glacier, but it was not until the final hours that the magma shot up towards the surface at Fimmvörðuháls. Although the build-up to the eruption had been long, and volcanic activity in the area was imminent, few people had anticipated that the magma would erupt at this location.

Late in the evening on Saturday 20 March, a fissure eruption began on the northern side of Fimmvörðuháls. The eruption was so small that its initiation barely registered on seismometers, so the first reports of it came from eyewitnesses in the Fljótshlíð area. Because it was not clear exactly where the magma had been erupted, the evacuation process was started, and people left the area that was thought to be at risk of sudden flooding (jökulhlaup) caused by the eruption. It soon became obvious, however, that the eruption was on Fimmvörðuháls, the ice-free ridge between Eyjafjallajökull and Mýrdalsjökull, so there was no immediate risk of flooding. The eruptive fissure was about 300 m long at first, and lava fountains rose along its

length, up to 100 m high. Straightaway, a gentle lava stream began to flow downhill from the eruption site, which was not far from the northern edge of the mountainous area. On Monday, only the second full day of the eruption, lava began to flow into Hrunagil, one of the gullies on the northern side of Fimmvörðuháls. A very beautiful lava-fall formed there because the floor of Hrunagil lies about 150 m below the mountain edge. Initially the heat of the lava was dissipated in melting a large snowdrift in the gully bottom, but a few days later lava began to flow down the gully, travelling about three kilometres along the gully floor before coming to a halt.

Fairly soon after the start of the eruption, activity became concentrated in one main crater on the original fissure, and it eventually reached a height of 80 metres. Eventually, the stream of lava towards the north lessened, and lava also began to flow westwards where it flowed into Hvannárgil in two places. On 31 March, after eleven days of volcanic activity, a new fissure opened

east of the main crater, and the flow of lava from it increased rapidly in the first few hours. Tourists had been walking around the area just before the fissure opened, and they probably narrowly escaped falling in to it. The new fissure subsequently produced another crater, 50 metres high, and the lava from it flowed west, down into Hvannárgil. Early in April, after the new fissure opened, volcanic activity gradually reduced. On the evening of 12 April, almost 23 days since the eruption began, activity is thought to have ceased. Two fairly high craters were left standing, surrounded by 1.3 km^2 of rough aa lava, about 10–20 m thick everywhere up on the ridge. That was the end of an interesting, but very small, event which was only the first half of the volcanic activity in Eyjafjallajökull that spring. Just over twenty-four hours later, another eruption began, this time in the summit crater of the central volcano. That eruption was of a completely different nature to the Fimmvörðuháls one, and characterised by a lot of explosive activity because meltwater from the glacier had easy access to the magma in the crater. This did not happen at Fimmvörðuháls though, so a gentle effusion of basalt lava occurred there, with little ash formation and little or no explosive activity. There is more about the eruption at the summit of Eyjafjallajökull in the next chapter.

The Fimmvörðuháls eruption was an amazing sight, and people flocked to see it, both from the land and the air. A stream of jeeps often lay over Mýrdalsjökull to the eruption sites, and people hiked onto the ridge, either from Skógar or Básar. Almost as soon as the eruption ended, tourists began to make their way over the new lava and up to the craters, and a new hiking trail was marked in the summer of 2010. It lies across the lava, above the crater Magni and around Móði, with detours up to both craters. Immediately after the eruption, the craters were rich with yellow, white, red and even green precipitations formed from gases issuing from the cooling lava. Many wrongly believe that the yellow colour in the precipitations is pure sulphur, but that is actually rare in volcanic precipitations, unlike geothermal ones in which sulphur is often found in large quantities. However, sulphur compounds, called sulphates, are common in the new lava, as are fluorine and chlorine compounds - sodium chloride for example, ordinary salt. Many of these precipitations are very delicate and disappear rapidly in rain. Now that some time has passed since the eruption ended, the original glorious colours have mostly given way to the red shades of scoria and volcanic slag. The lava still steams though, and four years after the end of the eruption, snow still did not linger in the summit crater. To conserve this remarkable and exciting environment it is important to stay on the marked trails - tracks criss-crossing a new landscape are a very ugly sight.

When the eruption had ended, the work of finding names for the new craters began. Many suggestions came from the public, and the Minister for Education appointed a working group to choose new names for the craters and the lava. On 15 June 2010, the group proposed new names that had already been positively received by locals in the Eyjafjallajökull area. It was proposed that the larger crater be named Móði, and the smaller one Magni; the lava was to be Goðahraun. Magni and Móði were sons of Þór in Norse mythology, and the new names reflected the many local place names derived from mythology, such as Þórsmörk and Goðaland. It is safe to say that they are suitable names, and that enjoying the new landscape on Fimmvörðuháls is something to look forward to in the future.

Eyjafjallajökull

Although few non-Icelanders can pronounce Eyjafjallajökull, many have heard of it – even though few can pronounce it properly. In 2010 there was an eruption in the summit crater of Eyjafjallajökull, and the volcano spewed an ash cloud south over the Atlantic ocean, to Europe. The ash in the upper atmosphere resulted in closure of a large part of European air space, so millions of travellers were stranded. Judging by reactions to the eruption, it might be assumed that this was one of the most troublesome volcanoes in the country, but this is not so. Although there is a risk of glacial floods (jökulhlaup), Eyjafjallajökull seldom erupts and all known eruptions in historical times have been relatively small scale.

Eyjafjallajökull is one of few Icelandic central volcanoes that can be termed a stratovolcano. High, cone-shaped volcanoes in other countries, like Mt. Fuji in Japan or Mt. Cotopaxi in Ecuador, are archetypal volcanoes to many people. Such volcanoes have built up over long periods of repeated erup-

tions, often in a summit crater. Most Icelandic central volcanoes are far from being so beautifully shaped; in fact they usually form irregular heaps in the landscape, often with a central caldera. There are some exceptions though: Snæfellsjökull, Öræfajökull and Eyjafjallajökull. These central volcanoes are certainly a little more convex than many foreign stratovolcanoes, but nevertheless they have steep sides and a summit crater, as well as being higher than other Icelandic volcanoes. Eyjafjallajökull is itself an oval ridge with an east-west trend, the dominating trend for fractures in the area, and it often erupts on the flanks outside the summit crater, as was seen in the Fimmvörðuháls eruption in the spring of 2010. The Eyjafjallajökull stratovolcano is one of the largest volcanoes in the country when the volcano's volume above its surroundings is measured. Because the easternmost part of the volcano merges with the western edge of Katla's caldera rim it is difficult to estimate the vol-

ume exactly, but it can be roughly calculated that Eyjafjallajökull measures between 230 and 270 km³. That is about 60-70% of the volume of Öræfajökull, Iceland's largest volcano, showing that Eyjafjallajökull is no small affair.

Eyjafjallajökull's eruption history is quite well known after Iceland's settlement period, but less so for the previous thousands of years. Eyjafjallajökull has erupted four times since Iceland was settled, first in the 10th century, when it is thought that Skerin, a ridge on the northwest side of the glacier, was formed. It also erupted at the start of the 17th century, early in the 19th century, and finally the most recent eruption happened in 2010. All the eruptions were relatively small, but they were doubtlessly all accompanied by a glacial flood or jökulhlaup – the volcano is covered by an icecap that is up to 200 m thick in the summit crater. The precipitously steep slopes provide perfect channels for the meltwater and mudflows to pour down to the lowlands. Floods have an open route down the southern slopes, and a small flood occurred there in the 2010 eruption. It is also thought that a medium-sized jökulhlaup flooded down the glacier on the southwest side in around the year 700, between Núpsheiði and Steinafjall. The main flood path, however, is north of the summit crater, down the Gígjökull outlet glacier to the Markarfljót river. Because there is a fairly large population living south of Eyjafjallajökull and on the Markarfljót plain, the flood risk is serious and the volcano is dangerous even though the eruptions

themselves are minor. Looking even further back in geological time, it can be seen that the volcano developed during many eruptions, both lava eruptions and explosive events, in glacial and interglacial periods. Eyjafjallajökull volcano's oldest rock occurs lowest on the south side of the mountain, and based on age-dating it is thought to be about 800,000 years old. This is fairly old for an Icelandic central volcano – their average life-span is thought to be about a million years old. So Eyjafjallajökull is a mature volcano, compared to Hekla, for example, which is still in its infancy.

Because of Eyjafjallajökull's eruptive history, geologists have been watchful of the mountain for some time. It has long been thought that a connection might exist between activity in Eyjafjallajökull and the volcano Katla beneath Mýrdalsjökull. Since Iceland's settlement, it appears that Katla has erupted at a similar time to Eyjafjallajökull, but no connection has been shown between them. In fact, the volcanoes are dissimilar in many ways, not least the infrequent eruptions of Eyjafjallajökull, while Katla is one of Iceland's most active volcanoes. Although central volcanoes obviously frequently respond to their environs, the movement and changes in other volcanic systems for example, it could just be sheer coincidence that Katla has erupted at or about the same time as Eyjafjallajökull. Whatever the case, Eyjafjallajökull has been monitored using seismometers since the middle of the last century, and in 1972-73 an excellent monitoring system was installed along the south coast in case of an imminent Katla eruption. From then on, Eyjafjallajökull has been under special surveillance, but nothing of note occurred in the volcano during those years. However, Eyjafjallajökull woke in 1992, and a series of earthquakes commenced, peaking in 1994. After this, it became evident that the crust had risen a little on the south side of the glacier, and it is thought that magma had forced its way up beneath the volcano, making a small intrusion. The same thing happened in 1999 when the ground south of the glacier rose about 10-20 cm in association with a powerful series of earthquakes.

Little of note happened in the early years of the new century, but at the end of 2009 this changed. A powerful series of earthquakes began, along with uplift, intensifying as 2010 progressed. At the end of February activity increased significantly, and it was obvious that something unusual was happening in the volcano. In early March, inhabitants on the south coast prepared themselves for a potential eruption, and in the middle of the month it was reported that magma was pushing higher into the crust. Late in the evening of 20 March, a small fissure eruption began on the north side of the Fimmvörðuháls ridge, described in the previous chapter. That eruption was small compared to most volcanic events in Iceland, but all the more interesting and unusual for the public. The Fimmvörðuháls eruption lasted almost 23 days, and probably ended in the evening of 12 April. About twenty-four hours later, just before midnight 13 April, another series of earthquakes began, this time below Eyjafjallajökull's summit crater. The earthquakes began at a few kilometres' depth but rapidly became shallower, and between one and two a.m. earthquake activity lessened and harmonic tremors began - these are continuous rhythmic vibrations. It is thought that at this point, magma had begun to flow up beneath the base of the glacier in the summit crater.

The eruption was small at first but strengthened rapidly in the first few hours, and waves of activity continued until the second half of May when ongoing activity ceased. The eruption was at the top of Eyjafjallajökull on a fissure about one or two metres in length, which stretched some distance onto the southern side of the mountain, although the main activity was in the summit crater itself. The first days of the eruption were characterised by a lot of explosive activity and ash formation. The chemistry of the magma was different from the basalt erupted in the Fimmvörðuháls eruption - this magma was more acidic (silica-rich), so it was more viscous and richer in gases, increasing the likelihood of explosive activity. In addition, there were powerful explosions when water entered the eruption conduit and mixed with the magma so that it shattered in steam explosions. In the explosions, the magma became a fine powder; unusually fine compared to most eruptions in Iceland, and this ash was carried by thermal currents several kilometres into the atmosphere. In the early days of the eruption, winds from the north and northwest blew the ash out to sea, and the finest particles were carried all the way to Scandinavia and Central Europe. Civil aviation authorities decided to close large portions of European airspace because of the ash which can get into jet engines and cause blockages. During the first five days of the eruption there were severe flight delays in Europe, and over 100,000 flight cancellations were caused by the eruption.

At the same time as the ash caused havoc in Europe, the eruption was causing trouble in the area around Eyjafjallajökull. In the first days of the eruption, a fairly large glacial outburst flood (jökulhlaup) came down Gígjökull, from the summit crater where magma melted the glacier ice, and a small flood also flowed down the southern slopes of Eyjafjallajökull. The first flood occurred in the morning immediately after the eruption began, but others of varying sizes followed over the next two days. The floods caused little damage, given their size. The Markarfljót river defences held for the most part, and both of the bridges over the Markarfljót withstood the assault, although the main road was deliberately breached in favour of the lower bridge, to reduce the pressure on it. The main long-term effects of the floods were on the glacial lake in front of the Gígjökull outlet glacier. The floods carried an enormous quantity of volcanic and glacial debris down onto the lowland, and at the end of the first eruption day, the lake had been completely filled with sediment from the floodwaters. A lot of ash fell in the area around the glacier too, much to the misery and inconvenience of the locals, but the lasting impact was small.

Most of the ash fell in the first few days, and on the fifth day the explosive activity was reduced, so ash production diminished. It is thought that water stopped getting into the magma in such large quantities at that time. A few days later, lava began to flow from the volcano, and it travelled down the water channel that had formed in the Gígjökull outlet glacier. By early March it had flowed about three kilometres down the slope, but it went no further. The eruption became explosive again on 5 May, with associated ash fall in the surrounding area, but the chemistry had changed and the magma was now similar to the magma erupted in the Fimmvörðuháls eruption. Earth scientists think that this was an eruption of some of the Fimmvörðuháls magma that had remained below the volcano since earlier in the spring. The eruption in Eyjafjallajökull's summit crater finally ended on 22 May and had lasted for 39 days. There was a final gasp in early June when small explosions were noticed in the summit crater, but Eyjafjallajökull was otherwise silent. How long it will remain silent is uncertain – judging by its eruptive history, activity is unlikely in the coming decades or even centuries. It is best, though, to say as little as possible about it; the behaviour of volcanoes like Eyjafjallajökull is not easy to predict.

Heimaey and Eldfell

Just before two in the morning on 23 January 1973, the townspeople of Vestmannaeyjar woke to a nightmare. A volcanic fissure had opened just two hundred metres from the easternmost houses on the island of Heimaey, and incandescent lava fountains rose well over a hundred metres into the air. It was the start of one of Iceland's most memorable and momentous eruptions in recent times. Around five thousand of the island's inhabitants had to flee in the night, and many people were unable to return to their old homes after the eruption ended. The town soon rose from the ashes, however, and it is now a blooming community once again, but the townspeople will always have a tangible reminder of the eruption, in the shape of the new lava.

The Vestmannaeyjar volcanic system lies southwest of the southernmost part of Iceland's East Volcanic Zone the zone that includes the Katla and Eyjafjallajökull volcanic systems. Some geologists think that activity in the Vestmannaeyjar volcanic system signals some sort of advance by the East Volcanic Zone, which appears to be extending southwards, and they point to the system's young age and the chemistry of the erupted material to support this. A new volcanic system seems to be forming there, and it is quite possible that in time a central volcano will develop on Heimaey, al-though this is a long process. Various things suggest that the system's volcanic activity is periodic, with intervals of a few thousand years in between, so the eruptions of Surtsey and Heimaey belong to a new period of volcanic activity. It is impossible to predict if there will be more of these eruptions in the immediate future, but there is nothing to suggest that volcanic activity in the Vestmannaeyjar archipelago will not continue, or even increase, in the future.

Activity in the Vestmannaeyjar volcanic system in the 20th century is remarkable in many ways. Surtsey formed in a long-lived eruption lasting from 1963 to 1967. In 1973 the eruption on Heimaey began, and it ercontinued until late in June the same year. Chemical analysis has shown that the magma erupted on Heimaey in 1973 was probably left-over magma from the Surtsey eruption. It appears to have rested in a magma chamber about 20 km below the islands for ten years before continuing upwards. The Heimaey eruption began as a fissure eruption, a few hundred metres long, just east of the town; but the fissure quickly lengthened to about 1500 m long, and stretched roughly from north to south, over the whole of the eastern part of the island. A series of earthquakes were recorded about twenty-four hours before the eruption, but

measurements at that time were not accurate enough to locate the earthquake swarm precisely under Heimaey, so the islanders were given no warning about the eruption. Fortunately, the fishing fleet was in harbour, and it was possible to transport almost all the inhabitants to the mainland in only a few hours. A few people stayed behind, and a difficult battle with the forces of nature took place, as people worked to save items of value was saved from the lava and falling pumice issuing from the volcano.

The eruption was most powerful at the beginning, and the eruptive fissure lengthened in several stages during January and February. The fissures had a total length of about 3.5 km, but the activity began to be concentrated on the central part of the fissure right from the start. A high scoria cone built up there, and it was the main site of the eruption while it lasted. In the first weeks the lava flowed mostly northwards and eastwards, and extended the island by about two square kilometres in less than a month. It was soon obvious that the lava could easily block the entrance to the harbour, and trials began to pump seawater onto the lava, to check its flow. The cooling had a noticeable effect, so larger pumps were obtained from the United States to cool the lava. In this way the lava flow was probably prevented from closing the entrance to the harbour – losing the harbour would have been a disaster for the town. The large pumps did not, however, arrive in time to stop the lava flow that threatened the town, and a large part of the town of Vestmannaeyjar was badly affected by the eruption. In the latter half of February, dozens of houses were buried when tephra, part of the new crater, slid down and flowed over the south-eastern part of the town, and soon after the middle of March the defence wall that had held back the lava gave way. In only a few days, starting on 22

March, 100 buildings were destroyed by the lava, and by the end of the eruption over two hundred houses in the town had buried under the lava or pumice, in addition to the many houses that were burned as a result of the glowing tephra that fell.

Gradually, the eruption diminished, and by the second half of April the flow of lava was minimal. Finally, on 3 July a visit was made to the crater, and the eruption was formally declared ended – no activity had been seen or heard since 26-28 June. At the end of the eruption, the main crater, which was about 200 m high then, was named Eldfell, or Fire Mountain, and the eastern side of it shows roughly where the coastline had been before the eruption. Reconstruction of the town began after the eruption, and it is now a thriving community. Although the fiery outburst had an enormous effect on the town, it was not all bad. Soon after the eruption ended, experiments began in which the new lava was used to heat water for use in district-heating, and the results were promising. Subsequently, the construction of the first (probably the only) lava-powered heating system on Earth began, and the first phase was commissioned in 1978, reaching full capacity shortly afterwards. The district's lava-heating system was designed so that when water was sprayed over the lava, it seeped down to the lava's hot core, which was still not solidified and up to 1000°C hot. Down in the lava, the water heated up to boiling point and changed to steam that rose upwards into a collection well. From there, the steam was piped to a heat exchanger and used to heat water for the space-heating system. Over time, utilisation cooled the lava at each place and the extraction system had to be moved to an unused area of lava. The district's lava-heating system was in use until 1988, but by when it was no longer profitable to use the heat from the cooling lava.

Surtsey

Surtsey is probably more difficult to visit than all the other places in this book. Surtsey formed in a prolonged eruption from 1963-1967, and it was given protected status in 1965. Since that time, visiting the island and its immediate surroundings has only been permitted for research purposes – and then only with special permission from the authorities. In 2008, Surtsey was accepted onto UNESCO's World Heritage List, gaining recognition as an important part of mankind's common natural heritage. The position awarded the island is largely thanks to its having been protected from the start, and it has always had a very important role as a sort of laboratory for geology and biology. Surtsey's unique status has made it possible to observe land colonisation by plants and birds right from the beginning, and biologists have carefully recorded all the new colonising species since that time. But while biologists have been studying the construction and development of the island's ecosystem, geologists have mostly had to watch the breakdown and destruction of the island. This is a natural process in geology though, and erosion began to demolish the island as soon as it peeped above the ocean's surface.

The Surtsey eruption was first noticed on the morning of 14 November 1963. The eruption had probably been simmering below for some time before that, but the depth of the seabed in this area was about 130 m before the eruption. Because of the water depth, the volcanic vent must have needed to build up for some time before the eruption reached the surface. Immediately on 14 November there were large steam explosions in which tephra (ash and larger particles) was hurled tens of metres up from the ocean's surface. The steam explosions happened when magma forced its way up onto the ocean floor, where it was suddenly cooled and shattered into tephra. Just a few hours after the eruption was first noticed, the eruption cloud had reached a height of over three kilometres, and by the second day it was about nine kilometres high. By then, a large heap of tephra had already built up, more than ten metres above sea level. Allowing for the ocean depth in the area, this means that a 140 m high mountain had already formed.

On the 9 December 1963, almost a month after the eruption started, the Ministry for Education announced the name of the new island. It would be known as Surtsey, and the eruption crater was named Surtur. The names referred to a black fire giant in Norse mythology, and they were chosen

because of the island's dark appearance. The eruption continued uninterrupted into the new year, and by the end of January, the island was at a height of 174 m. At the end of that month, the eruption in Surtur stopped, but two days later it began again in a new crater, northwest of the old one. The new crater was simply named Surtur II, to differentiate it from the older one, but it is also often called Surtungur. On 4 April the younger Surtur finally became isolated from the ocean, and an effusive eruption of lava began from a lava pond in the crater. Lava poured from the crater towards the sea, and soon formed a thick lava field, over 100 m thick closest to the crater. The lava eruption continued until May 17 1965, when it ended after lasting more than a year, leaving an island 2.4 km² in area. Another eruption began in Surtsey about a year later, on 16 August, and it continued until June 1967. Lava poured, from new craters in the place where the older Surtur had erupted. The lava covered a considerable area south and southeast of the craters. When the eruption ended, the island was 2.7 km² in area and about 1.1 km³ of material had been erupted. Of that, 60-70% was tephra and 30-40% was lava.

While Surtsey was growing, there were also a few eruptions in the sea to the southwest. Two other new islands were created there, and one eruption occurred without producing an island. The two islands were named Syrtlingur and Jólnir, but because the eruptions did not last long enough to produce lava flows, the islands were easily eroded and soon disappeared back into the sea. Surtsey, however, has withstood the sea's encroachment despite considerable erosion, and this is largely because of the lava produced in the eruption. In 1975, the area of Surtsey had been reduced to about two square kilometres, and by 2002 it was 1.4 km². In recent years erosion has averaged about 0.01 km² each year, which is not much compared to the early years after the eruption ended.

Contrary to what many people think, it is not the lavas which will guarantee a long life for the island, although their existence was necessary. The lavas that flowed from Surtsey are cracked and relatively easily eroded, but they are the reason why hydrothermal activity began in the island soon after the eruption ended. In 1968-69 hydrothermal activity was first noticed in the centre of the island, and it has been linked to the feeder dykes that supplied the lava craters. Sea is able to seep easily through the base of the island, into the middle of the lavas where it heats up and then rises. The hydrothermal system formed in this way makes the island's piles of tephra harden, and it becomes móberg (palagonite tuff). Studies of the móberg formations on Surtsey have shown that the hardening of volcanic ash into móberg takes place over a much shorter time than was previously thought. At temperatures above 100°C, the móberg becomes fully hardened after one year, or even less. At lower temperatures this happens over a longer time, but still relatively quickly. The formation of móberg is very important for the lifetime of the island because the móberg centre is much harder than the lava. So it is the móberg which will resist the sea longest, and eventually Surtsey will end as a rock in the sea, surrounded on all sides by móberg cliffs. The sea has already eroded into the móberg on the western side of the island and made sea cliffs, over 100 m high. It has been argued that this will be Surtsey's fate in the not too distant future, and the Icelandic Institute of Natural History's model predicts that the Clarify may be reached after about 160 years. Then Surtsey will look like other outposts in the Vestmannaeyjar archipelago, such as Bjarnarey which is thought to have formed about 5000-6000 years ago.

Hekla

In other countries, Hekla was for centuries the best known of all Iceland's landmarks. Stories about the volcano were so terrible that most people considered the mountain to be the entrance to Hell itself. For those of us who have only encountered the relatively small "tourist-eruptions" that have happened in Hekla in the last decade, it is perhaps difficult to understand the terror induced by Hekla's past eruptions. The truth is that eruptions in Hekla were usually dreadful events and no wonder that they have been among the greatest causes of terror in the lives of Hekla's neighbours throughout history. Of all the Icelandic volcanoes, Hekla is really in a class by itself, or possibly with Katla, when it comes to destruction and threat to life and limb.

But what sort of volcano is Hekla? It is one of Iceland's many central volcanoes – these are volcanoes that erupt repeatedly and build themselves into a mountain. Hekla stands out from the group, however, both because of how young it is and because of its appearance. It is an elongate stratovolcano, and it usually erupts on a fissure that runs the length of the mountain – referred to simply as Heklugjá, Hekla's fissure. It is thought that the mountain did not begin to build up, to any real degree, until some years after regional glaciation ended. The first known "large" eruption from Hekla is believed to have happened about 7000 years ago, but small effusive eruptions of lava probably took place before this. Since the first large eruption, there have been a few enormous eruptions and innumerable small ones, and in this way the mountain has built up over the last few millennia. Consequently, Hekla is virtually a brand-new central volcano, younger than most, if not all, other evolved Icelandic central volcanoes, some of which are a few hundred thousand years old.

Hekla is thought to have erupted 18 times since Iceland's settlement. First it erupted in 1104, and that was the volcano's

largest eruption in historical times. It was an enormous explosive eruption, and the mountain spewed a tremendous quantity of ash and pumice (tephra) over the island's inhabitants, so destruction was widespread. A flourishing community was to be found in the vicinity of the mountain at this time, in the Þjórsárdalur valley west of Mt. Búrfell, but the area was destroyed by the eruption. Old farm ruins have been excavated in the area at Stöng and Skeggjastaðir, evidence of the devastation. This first eruption was only the start of Hekla's career. Since then it has often caused severe damage, and the eruptions of 1510, 1693 and 1766–68 were particularly burdensome.

The start of an eruption in Hekla is usually accompanied by heavy falls of tephra, and it is this aspect of Hekla's eruptions that has proved worst for the Icelandic people. Close to the volcano, the tephra has frequently been so thick that farmsteads have been abandoned because of it. Air pollution also accompanies the eruptions. Ash from Hekla is usually rich in fluorine, which coats the fine ash particles. It binds calcium in animal fodder and causes a calcium deficiency in livestock that manifests as bone and dental diseases such as gaddur and doði, deformed bones and debility. Lava,

on the other hand, has usually been less of a threat, partly because lava from Hekla is viscous, so it flows a shorter distance than lavas from many other volcanoes. Also, the area closest to the volcano has always been sparsely populated. Nevertheless, farms are believed to have been destroyed by lava in the 1389 eruption, and in 1845 the farm buildings at Næfurholt had to be moved after a tongue of lava from Hekla flowed alarmingly close to the farm.

Hekla is an extremely young volcano and one of the most active in Iceland. Its eruption history since the settlement period is well known from official records. The story of Hekla's eruptions before Iceland was settled is, however, told by the layers of tephra in soil cross-sections. Well-known volcanologist Sigurður Þórarinsson was the first scientist to study tephra layers from Hekla in his doctoral thesis in 1944, laying the foundations for tephrachronology which is used to date archaeological remains and geological events based on the known ages of tephra layers. Three of Hekla's enormous eruptions have been recognised from the period before Iceland was settled, as well as a number of smaller ones. The three large eruptions produced very distinctive tephra layers that can be

distinguished fairly readily from ash layers of other volcanoes by their thickness and light colour. These tephra layers have been named Hekla 3 (H3), Hekla 4 (H4) and Hekla 5 (H5), depending on where they are found in the soil. In the soil profile, H5 is the lowest of the tephra layers, and also the oldest, produced in an enormous explosive eruption about 7100 years ago. H4 was erupted about 4300 years ago, and H3 about 3000 years ago – this last eruption was the largest Hekla eruption of all time. The ages are based on carbon-dating of organic material that has been found in or next to the tephra layers.

One feature of the Hekla eruptions is displayed in the H4 tephra layer. The layer typically has two different colours – in most places it is light at the bottom and dark at the top. This is because the erupted magma changed in composition as the eruption progressed. This applies to other eruptions from Hekla too, particularly the largest ones. At first acid magma is erupted, with a high proportion of silica relative to ordinary basalt lava. This acid magma produces light-coloured pumice and ash, similar in composition to rhyolite, but as the eruption continues, the magma erupted becomes poorer in silica and produces darker and darker ash. In some eruptions, such as H4,

the division between light and dark pumice is very sharp. Another characteristic of Hekla's eruptions is that the longer the interval between them, the bigger they are. The largest eruptions in Hekla have come after long periods of rest, probably a few hundred years. The 1104 Hekla eruption was the last big eruption, and at that time Hekla had not erupted since before Iceland was first settled, at least 250 years. The ash layer from the 1104 eruption is noticeably light-coloured, as are all ash layers from big eruptions, and it is sometimes called Hekla 1 (H1). The reason for Hekla's changing magma composition during eruptions is not beyond dispute, but various details in Hekla's eruptive behaviour and the composition of the magma suggest that a magma chamber lies deep below Hekla, probably at over 14 km depth. If a long time passes between eruptions, it seems that the magma in the magma chamber manages to melt older rock, and this produces some lower density rhyolite magma, which is the first magma to be erupted in large eruptions. However, the presence of the magma chamber has not been conclusively proven, and so there is still a lack of basic knowledge about this great volcano. It is only in the largest of Hekla's eruptions that rhyolite magma is erupted; the lava from Hekla is otherwise intermediate, with a composition between rhyolite and basalt.

Hekla's eruptive behaviour in historical times is well known. From the start of the 12th century until the middle of the 20th, it erupted at roughly 60-year intervals on average. The largest eruption in the 20th century was in 1947 when the mountain erupted after an interval of 101 years – it had previously erupted in 1845–46. One of the most famous photographs of a Hekla eruption is from the start of the eruption on 29 March 1947, showing the 28 km high eruption cloud only 20 minutes after the eruption started. The picture was taken east of Reykjavík, over 120 km away from Hekla, and the magnificence of the eruption is perfectly caught. Since this large eruption in 1947, however, Hekla's behaviour has changed. Instead of waiting several decades as expected, Hekla erupted again in 1970; and again in 1980–81, 1991 and 2000, but all these eruptions were minor compared to earlier ones.

Hekla appears, therefore, to have changed tempo, for the time being at least – instead of many decades, an average of about ten years has passed between the last four eruptions. Between eruptions, Hekla and the surrounding land rise, indicating that magma is flowing into the magma chamber below the mountain. When there is an eruption the land sinks again, at the same time as the mountain pours out ash and lava. At the time of this book's publication in the spring of 2016, Hekla will have risen more than before the eruptions in 1991 and 2000. Judging by its behaviour in recent eruptions, it is "ready to blow", so to speak, and it might not be long until the next eruption. The behaviour of volcanoes is unpredictable though, and it is also possible that Hekla's behaviour will change again, and that it will be a long time until the next eruption. Hiking on Hekla has been popular, and the view from the top is truly amazing. However, the warning time before an eruption in Hekla is very short – before the 2000 eruption, it was less than an hour. So, it could be dangerous to climb the volcano under the current circumstances, since an advance warning of an eruption does not allow enough time to hike off the mountain.

Gullfoss

Gullfoss is one of Iceland's best-known landmarks, both at home and abroad. The waterfall has long been intertwined with the national consciousness, and it could be called one of the principal symbols of unification for Icelanders. Gullfoss has been a very popular tourist attraction since the 19th century, and now over 70% of overseas guests visit the waterfall each year. Although many people feel that the number of tourists in the area is a bit too high, especially in summer, such feelings usually disappear as soon as the waterfall comes into view. Few things equal the experience of water-spray on the face and hearing the rumble of the torrent as it hits the canyon floor. Elemental power exists not only in the waterfall though, but also in the canyon below it, the banks on each side, and the erosional forces that have shaped the land in this region.

The geological story of Gullfoss and its surrounding area is one of rapidly changing landscape. During the Ice Age, a thick glacier lay over the highlands, and carved and smoothed the land beneath it. About ten thousand years ago, when the Ice Age glacier melted, it had removed more or less all signs of any previous canyons or water channels in the area. The powers of erosion had to begin digging again, and they did not hold back. Now, ten thousand years later, they have been so successful that a roughly three-kilometre-long canyon, Hvítárgljúfur, has been cut in the margin of the highlands. Geologists have not been able to agree about how this happened, and two principle theories have been advanced regarding the canyon formation. On the one hand, some argue that constant river erosion dug the canyon steadily over the last ten thousand years, and on the other hand, it is argued that a few enormous cataclysmic floods at the end of glaciation eroded the canyon over a short time.

Gullfoss falls 32 m in total, in two unequally sized steps which are about 10 and 20 metres high, respectively. The waterfall's two steps are made of basalt lavas of different thicknesses, and between them is an easily eroded sedimentary layer. Downstream of Gullfoss is the canyon Hvítárgljúfur, which is up to 70 m deep. The canyon is terraced to some degree, and this can be easily seen by looking from the waterfall, down along the river. In the middle of the canyon is a wide shelf, below the lower car park, which can be said to divide the river into a wide upper part and narrow lower part. Using tephrachronology, Icelandic geologist Þorleifur Einarsson concluded that the river had eroded the canyon gradually, and that the southern part of it was oldest, and the northernmost part youngest. He based this conclusion on tephra layers from the volcano Hekla. Furthest south in the canyon, he found a roughly 6600-year-old tephra horizon, the H5 layer (see chapter on Hekla), but to the north he found increasingly younger layers. Closest to Gullfoss, even the tephra layer from Hekla's 1766 eruption was missing, and he thought that this part of the canyon formed after that eruption. Based on this, Þorleifur decided that the three-kilometre-long canyon had been gradually eroded over the last ten thousand years, and that the erosion rate was about 30 cm each year.

Another Icelandic geologist, Haukur Tómasson, disagreed with Þorleifur and thought that the canyon had formed in vast cataclysmic floods towards the end of the last glaciation. Actually, Þorleifur did not disagree that cataclysmic floods had occurred in the highlands, north of Kjölur, but he thought that they had not contributed to the erosion of the canyon. Haukur worked in the Kjölur area a lot, studying the river Hvítá's catchment area because of a proposed hydropower station. At Kjölur, old shorelines can be widely seen, marking the water level in old glacial lakes. The shorelines are like horizontal lines in the landscape, on the slopes of Hrútfell and other nearby mountains, for example.

From research on the shorelines and glacial striations (scratches made by moving ice) at Kjölur, it is possible to show that the mid-point of the highland ice mass lay a bit further south than the current centre of the highlands. The Ice Age glacier was therefore thickest some distance south of Kjölur, and when it retreated at the end of glaciation, it vanished early north of Kjölur, but remained longer in the southern highlands. When the ice had disappeared from the highest part of Kjölur, a glacial lake formed there, dammed by a glacier tongue south of Mt. Bláfell. At first the lake drained to the north, and there are widespread signs of large floods along the course of the river Blanda. The best way to appreciate this is by driving along Kjalvegur (road F35), east of Hveravellir. The road goes straight over a number of dried-up water courses in the sand plain. These channels lie on Kjölur's bone-dry watershed, where it is hard to imagine that there was ever a river big enough to make them. The existence of glacial lakes south of the watershed explains the water channels rather well.

There were also sudden floods southwards from the glacial lakes, first across Bláfellsháls, north of Mt. Bláfell. There, just west of the road Kjalvegur, a dry canyon called Kór can be seen. It is easy to reach by walking about one kilometre along the Grjótá river. The most cataclysmic floods, however, occurred east of Bláfell, where the glacier tongue remained at its greatest length period of time. There are enormous flood channels alongside the mountain, and Haukur Tómasson thought that they were formed in a number of huge floods of various sizes. From the size of the flood channels, Haukur calculated the size of the floods, and he estimated that the flow rate in the first and largest flood was up to 300,000-400,000 m^2/s. That is about twice the average flow rate of the Amazon, and comparable to the largest outburst flood caused by the Katla volcano in the last century. Lower down in the highland region, the flood channels are less easy to see – the land there is flatter and the water more spread out. However, at the edge of the highlands, where the Hvítá canyon is now, the flow rate of the flood-water increased again and the erosion was enormous. In the Hvítá canyon it is possible to deduce this erosion from the shape of the canyon. The southern part of it, below the dell called Pjaxi, is very wide. Today the river Hvítá winds around gravel bars there, and its erosion power is limited. The canyon there is really too wide to have been eroded by the river, based on the current flow. The north-ern part of the canyon is divided in two by a shelf. The upper part, above the shelf, is as wide as the southern part of the canyon, and it was formed in the last cataclysmic floods. Since they were smaller, they did not erode as deep a canyon as the previous floods. The deeper section of the canyon, on the other hand, is much narrower, and the river fills the canyon floor. Haukur thought that that was a sign of active canyon-making by the current Hvítá river, and that this part was therefore eroded by the river in the thou-sands of years since the last glaciation.

One of the most significant and clever arguments against the idea of steady ero-sion of the canyon, advanced by Haukur, is a comparison of old and new photographs of Gullfoss. If the canyon had eroded gradually over the last ten thousand years, then the av-erage erosion by the river would have been about 30 cm each year. So the river should have lengthened by about 30 metres in the last hundred years, but when photographs of the canyon taken in the 19th century are compared to recent photographs, it appears that few or no changes have taken place. If only for this reason, it seems that Haukur's theory about the formation of the Hvítá can-yon and Gullfoss is more robust than Þorleif-ur's theory about steady erosion.

Finally, it is worth mentioning Gullfoss's role in the history of nature conservation in Iceland. The story of how Sigríður Tómasdótt-ir from Brattholt fought to save the waterfall early in the 20th century is quite famous. By her relentless campaigning it seems like-ly that she saved the waterfall from being harnessed for hydropower production, and her name will always be held aloft, entwined with the history of Gullfoss and nature con-servation in Iceland. But, although few would dream of harnessing Gullfoss now, there are still plans to build power stations in the high-lands above Gullfoss, in Hvítá and Jökulfall, as well as at the Hagavatn lake. Such plans would have a great effect on the waterfall and its setting, by altering the natural flow rate of Hvítá, for example. The indirect effect of such constructions are, however, even more important because the disturbance would change the status of the waterfall on the edge of the highlands. Gullfoss is an important part of the whole highland envi-ronment, and the waterfall acts as its south-ern advocate. Any change to the untouched highland wilderness above Gullfoss would damage the waterfall's status, and under-mine the position that it holds in our minds.

Geysir and Strokkur

Geysir is probably Iceland's best-known geological phenomenon. For centuries it was one of the only known geysers in the Western world, and its name has found its way into many other languages as the generic name for geysers. There are, numerous other active geysers here in Iceland, but Geysir is the greatest and has carried the name of Iceland around the globe. Geyser activity in the Geysir area fluctuates considerably, and Geysir itself is mostly dormant now. Strokkur, however, erupts continually and usually only a few minutes pass between eruptions. It is easy to get to the area, and it is no wonder that travellers have made their way there over the centuries. It does not really matter how often Strokkur is visited - the eruptions are always magnificent events.

The Geysir area is generally thought to be part of an independent volcanic system that was active a few hundred thousand years ago. To find signs of this old central volcano, it is possible to examine the mountain Laugarfjall, above the geyser area. It is mostly made of rhyolite, and there are also rhyolite patches on Mt. Bjarnafell. Other than this, the high temperature geothermal field at Geysir is the only remainder of the Geysir central volcano that lies furthest east in Iceland's active western volcanic zone. The high temperature geothermal area extends over about 3 km^2 and includes numerous springs, but the central fenced-off Geysir area is only about 0.2 km^2. Many of the springs in the area have names; the best known ones are Geysir and Strokkur. Among the others are Blesi, Konungshver, Fata, Óþerrishola and Smiður. Some of these springs are also geysers, but do not usually erupt of their own accord.

The oldest records mentioning Geysir date from the late 13th century. In 1294 there were major earthquakes in South Iceland, and the geysers in Haukadalur valley

were first mentioned in the annals after that. Well-known Icelandic geologist Sigurður Þórarinsson investigated the possible age of Geysir and the hot spring area in the mid-20th century, with the help of tephra layers. He came to the conclusion that the spring area was many thousands of years old, and had even been active since the time when the glaciers melted at the end of the last glaciation. Geysir's bowl could, however, be younger, and Geysir might even have been created in the earthquakes of 1294. Whether Geysir was first formed then or was revived after sleeping for a few centuries, it was intermittently active in the following centuries. It was most active after large earthquakes in South Iceland, as in 1630, following which it displayed enormous eruptions. In between active periods it is less energetic, and people have often resorted to putting stones and pieces of turf in the hot spring to get it to erupt. Geysir woke again in the 1896 earthquakes and erupted a few times a day, but by about 1915 it was dormant again. In 1935 a channel was dug through Geysir's sinter bowl, to lower its water level, and after this it began to erupt again. Over time, the channel filled again with sinter, and in 1981 it was re-dug and deepened. After that, Geysir was often made to erupt, especially on the August bank holiday weekend, and the eruptions were amazing spectacles. They were triggered by opening the channel, and a generous amount of soap was also added to the spring a little while before the eruption. Soap lowers the surface tension of the water and makes it easier for the super-heated water to come to a boil. After the South of Iceland earthquake in 2000, Geysir became slightly livelier and splashed a little, but now Geysir's enormous bowl is almost silent.

The other principal hot spring in the area, Strokkur, erupts regularly and is now the main visitor attraction. Strokkur's activity has also fluctuated, and while Geysir has been dormant, Strokkur has frequently been very active. Strokkur's largest eruptions in the 19th century are said to have lasted an hour and reached a height of up to 60 m. Like its partner though, Strokkur had lain dormant for decades when a decision was made to to drill about 40 metres into the sinter bowl in 1963. Following this, Strokkur has been very active and erupted every few minutes.

In earlier years there were several theories regarding the reasons for Geysir's eruptive activity. In 1846 Robert Bunsen, the famous chemist, came to Iceland. He examined Geysir and his theories about the activity have mostly stood the test of time. Like other erupting springs, Geysir consists of a narrow water pipe that extends deep into the ground. Measurements have shown that the pipe is about 40-100 cm wide at a depth of 23 m, but below that it narrows and becomes irregular, so that measuring its width becomes difficult. Bunsen measured the temperature in the water pipe at different depths, down to the bottom, and found that the upper levels of water are considerably below boiling point, at about 85-95°C. At a depth of 23 m, the temperature of the water is about 120°C, but because of the great pressure exerted by the water column above, it is still well below boiling point. However, midway in the water pipe, at about 15 m depth, the water's temperature reaches boiling point, and little disturbance is required to initiate boiling. When the water boils and becomes steam, its volume increases 1700-fold and the steam pushes the water column upwards. When boiling water produces large bubbles, the bumping they cause in a section of the water pipe causes a chain reaction; all the water in the pipe boils and pushes the only way available – through the hot-spring's opening.

Spouting hot springs do not, however,

all behave the same. Strokkur spouts small but powerful eruptions, up to 30 m high. The water channel does not empty between each eruption, so it fills again quickly, and it is not long before the next eruption. However, when Geysir was in its prime it behaved quite differently. An eruption in Geysir took longer and was many times more powerful. A Geysir eruption can be split into four phases of different lengths. The first phase is really a precursor to the eruption, when great turbulence and bangs begin to be noticed at the surface. This indicates bumping, when part of the water column, high in the pipe, reaches boiling point. After this, Geysir begins to splash a little. The bursts of water reach ten to twenty metres high, and this phase lasts for ten to fifteen minutes. Although the bursts are impressive, it is only the upper layers in the water pipe that take part in the eruption at this stage. The lower part of the water column is still calm, and after considerable splashing, silence descends on the area again for thirty to sixty seconds. At this point in time, pressure in the water pipe has fallen appreciably after the splashing, and the drop in pressure lowers the boiling point of the remaining water deeper in the conduit. Then bumping suddenly begins in the whole water pipe, and boiling water is sent along it and up to 60-80 metres above the sinter bowl. It is the most impressive phase of the eruption and lasts a few minutes until the pipe has emptied itself. After that the eruption continues for five to ten minutes, but now as a furious steam eruption. Little by little the eruption dies away, and the pipe begins to fill again. It takes about eight to ten hours for the hot spring to refill.

Astonishing as it is, Geysir has still not been given conservation status. The Icelandic State owns part of the hot spring area, including Strokkur, Geysir, Blesi and the land between them, but the remainder of the Geysir area is privately owned, and public access to it has been hotly disputed in recent years. Maintenance and facilities within the area have been very unsatisfactory, and far from a credit to Iceland, considering that several hundred foreign tourists visit the area every year. The saddest example of poor management was in 1981 when the channel in the sinter basin was widened, virtually under cover of night. In 1984 geologist Helgi Torfason wrote about this damage to nature at Geysir. He ended his article with the following words, "It is traditional in Iceland to mistreat the country and all its bounty, both on land and at sea. When will we attain the spiritual maturity to live in harmony with this barren land, let alone with each other?" The history of the Geysir area through the centuries is perhaps crystallised in these words. Hopefully the Geysir area will soon have better facilities, so that it is possible to treat it with the respect it deserves.

Kerið and the Grímsnes volcanic system

Kerið is the name of an impressive crater in the middle of the Grímsnes area. The place is a popular stopping point for tourists on the "Golden Circle". Kerið does not look like much from a distance, but once on the crater rim a wide and deep crater can be seen, over 250 m in diameter and more than 50 m deep. For many years Kerið was thought to have formed in an explosive eruption, but this has been shown to be incorrect. At the bottom of Kerið is a pretty lake which gives the place a fairytale ambiance, and the area's setting is both magnificent and wild.

The geology of the Grímsnes volcanic system, including Kerið and other craters and lavas in the area, was described in the 1960s and '70s. Kerið is the northernmost crater in a short crater row that has been called Tjarnarhólar. The other craters may be seen southwest of Kerið. A considerable quantity of lava flowed westwards from this eruptive fissure, across the Grímsnes area. It was long thought that Kerið was a good example of an explosive crater with a crater lake in its bottom – what has been called "maar" in other countries. It has been pointed out, however, that it is impossible to trace any major ash layer to Kerið, as would be normal if it had been formed in an explosive eruption. This suggests that Kerið was originally just an ordinary scoria cone. To explain the unusual depth of Kerið, it is thought that towards the end of the Tjarnarhólar eruption, a pool of magma in the bottom of Kerið emptied. Following this, the crater collapsed and Kerið took on the form that we recognise now. Soon after the eruption, the local groundwater began to flow into the crater. At first it was boiling hot, but gradually it cooled to the same temperature as the surrounding groundwater.

The Tjarnarhólar crater row eruption

was only one of twelve postglacial eruptions in the Grímsnes area. Together, these
twelve volcanoes are thought to belong to
the Grímsnes volcanic system, and the lava
from them covers a total area of 54 km².
The lavas appear to have been formed in
several events about 7000–9500 years
ago. The area's three largest eruptions
were at Seyðishólar, Kerhóll and Tjarnarhólar, and the eruption that formed the
Seyðishólar craters was largest. What char-
acterises the Seyðishólar craters is how full
of "air" the scoria forming them is – this is
thought to indicate that an unusually gas-
rich magma was erupted there. After 1980,
drilling for hot water took place on the
Hæðarendi property in Grímsnes, just north
of Seyðishólar. Quite a lot of hot water was
obtained from the hole, but the water was
rich in dissolved solids. It was also very gas-
rich and over 99% of the gas was carbon dioxide (CO_2). The inhabitants at Hæðarendi
subsequently began processing the carbon
dioxide, and now the only carbon dioxide
plant in Iceland is operated there. It is not
clear why the Grímsnes volcanic system is
so gas-rich, but usually carbon dioxide-rich
hydrothermal fluids have been linked to
cooling intrusions in the crust. In the case
of Grímsnes it has even been suggested
that the volcanic system is an example of a

central volcano in its final stage of development, and that it has been buried by younger basalt lavas. The chemical composition
of the lavas and geothermal fluids in the
area support this interpretation, although
further research is needed. As for the carbon dioxide plant at Hæðarendi – the original borehole is sufficient to supply all the
carbon dioxide needed in the country. Since
all Icelandic carbonated drinks are produced with carbon dioxide from Hæðarendi,
it could be said that Icelandic fizzy drinks
are made with volcanic gas.

In recent years Kerið has not only been
in the news because of its natural beauty.
Like various other popular tourist spots, especially those in the lowlands, Kerið and its
environs are privately owned, and disputes
have arisen about access. Two things can
be highlighted regarding this. One, the construction of facilities for tourists in the area
has been financed by public money, both
through the Icelandic Road Administration
and the Icelandic Tourist Board. And two,
the natural beauty of the country belongs
to all Icelanders, and limiting access to natural wonders in any manner, should not be
permitted except in very rare exceptions,
and then only for reasons of nature conservation.

Þingvellir

Þingvellir is one of the most remarkable geological sites in Iceland, and in fact it has world-class status. This is because the consequences of diverging tectonic plate movement can be seen there. Iceland is one of very few places on Earth where this can be seen on dry land. Although signs of plate spreading can be seen quite widely across the country, Þingvellir is a particularly convenient place to examine it because of the geological conditions there.

But what are diverging tectonic plates? The earth's crust is divided into a number of vast tectonic plates that extend over whole continents. The continent of North America is on one plate, and Europe and Asia are together on the enormous Eurasian tectonic plate. The tectonic plates meet at plate boundaries, which can be of three types. First, there are plate boundaries where two tectonic plates meet and push against each other along a collision zone called a convergent boundary. These sorts of plate boundaries are characterised by extremely big earthquakes that occur when tension between the plates is freed. Ranges of fold mountains, such as the Himalayas and the Andes, are often found along this type of boundary. The opposite type of plate boundary occurs where two tectonic plates move apart from each other, on a spreading zone. New crust is formed at such plate boundaries because eruptions continually occur between the plates as they move apart. This type of plate boundary is usually only found in the earth's oceans, along what are called oceanic ridges. In the middle of the Atlantic Ocean lies the Mid-Atlantic Ridge, and Iceland sits on its northern part. So, the divergent plate boundary between the North American plate and the Eurasian plate crosses Iceland, and the plates are moving apart by about two centimetres a year. The third type of plate boundary is called a transform boundary, where the tectonic plates slide past each other. This

process occurs in the South Iceland Seismic Zone.

As most people will probably appreciate, the movement of the tectonic plates in Iceland is such a slow process that it is impossible to just watch it happening in real time. It requires special circumstances to discern it in the environment. The reason why plate separation can be seen so well at Þingvellir is that shortly after the end of regional glaciation, around 10,000 years ago, there were some big eruptions in the Þingvellir area. Previously, eruptions had occurred under the Ice Age glacier and formed the móberg (hyaloclastite) ridges and mountains that are found in the area; but after the land became ice free, enormous shield volcanoes formed. Skjaldbreiður is the most prominent of them, but the lava fields that are spread across the Þingvellir National Park probably formed in several eruptions from various volcanoes, such as the Eldborgir lava which lies between Hrafnabjörg and Kálftindur northeast of Lake Þingvallavatn. The volume of lava erupted from these lava shields was enormous, which is convenient because it filled in all the unevenness and gaps that existed in the area. At the end of these eruptions, the lava expanse (where the Þingvellir valley is now) looked fairly even.

However, because the area lies on an active divergent plate boundary, its appearance has changed over the few thousand years since the volcanic activity. In this interval the eastern edge of the Þingvellir area has become distanced from the western edge because of plate tectonics. Plate movement in the Þingvellir area is thought to be only about 3-4 mm a year, which means that in 10,000 years the edges of the area have moved apart by about 30-40 m. When the plate margins move apart in this manner, the area between them subsides and a graben forms. The volcanic eruptions

which happened on the north side of the Þingvellir graben after the end of glaciation restarted the clock in that area. We know the age of the eruptions, and know roughly how the area looked after the eruptions, so now we can see many thousand years of geological history right in front of us.

Some misunderstanding has occasionally arisen about the plate boundary at Þingvellir. Most people assume that at Þingvellir the divergent boundary between the North American plate and the Eurasian plate can be seen, but this is not actually so. The plate boundaries in southern Iceland are a little more complicated because the boundary between the two large tectonic plates is in two parts. On the one hand, a plate boundary lies along the West Volcanic Zone, from Hengill, north through Þingvellir, up to Langjökull and then straight across Hofsjökull to the East Volcanic Zone. On the other hand, there is a plate boundary through the South Iceland Seismic Zone, the transform fracture zone where most of the largest South Iceland earthquakes occur, and the plate boundary goes from there over to the East Volcanic Zone at Torfajökull, and then northwards across the country. In between sits a small bit of Iceland, defined by the South Iceland Seismic Zone in the south, the West Volcanic Zone in the west, Hofsjökull volcanic system in the north, and the East Volcanic Zone to the east. This bit of Iceland belongs to neither the North American plate nor the Eurasian plate – instead it is regarded as an independent tectonic plate, a sort of micro-plate. It is called the Hreppa plate, and it moves independently relative to the two large plates on either side of it. So at Þingvellir it is possible to see the plate boundary between the North American plate and the Hreppa plate.

Another thing connected to the plate boundaries at Þingvellir sometimes causes misunderstanding too – where exactly does

the plate boundary lie? The plate boundary is in fact not a narrow line; rather it is a wide area. At Almannagjá on the west side of Lake Þingvallavatn, it is possible to see a sort of edge for the North American plate. A corresponding edge for the Hreppa plate is on the other side of the lake where Hrafnagjá is the main fissure. Between these two fissures is a five-kilometre-wide area which it is not possible to say belongs to one plate or the other. But the picture is not even that simple, because if the land is viewed in a wider context, two large faults can be seen either side of the Þingvellir area. It has been suggested that the faults on the eastern slopes of Mt. Botnssúlur and the western side of Mt. Laugarvatnsfjall form the outer edges of the Þingvellir graben, and this illustrates even better that the plate boundaries are certainly not defined lines – they are wide areas.

Þingvellir is not only important to the history of the Icelandic Nation, but also to the geological history of Iceland. Signs of tectonic plate movement are rarely seen as well as they are at Þingvellir, chiefly because magma has not moved under the area or flowed across it for a long time, so tectonic plate movement has produced a large graben. The Þingvellir graben is therefore not typical for a divergent plate boundary; actually it is an unusual feature. One of the best places to view the plate boundary is from the edge of the fissures on either side of Lake Þingvallavatn. From the brink of Almannagjá, the graben can be seen well, with a close net of northeast-southwest trending fractures on either side of the graben. Readers should also pay Mt. Ármannsfell particular attention. By looking carefully, it is possible to make out a large fault straight through the mountain, like an extension of Almannagjá, forming a sort of shoulder on the eastern side of the mountain. To get an even better overall idea of the region, it is good to climb either Mt. Arnarfell, east of the lake, or Ármannsfell itself, and see the area from a greater height.

Highlands

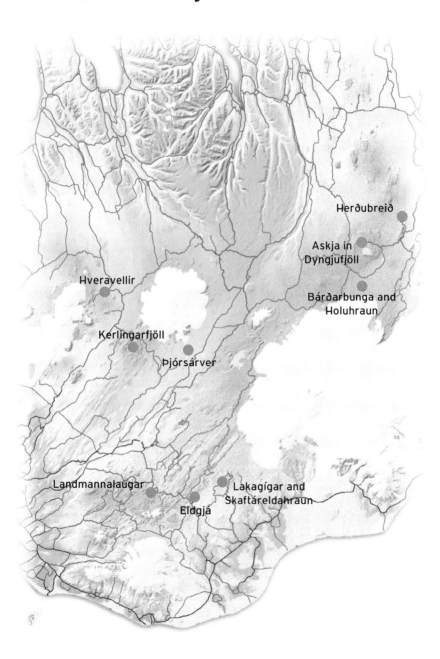

Herðubreið

Askja in Dyngjufjöll

Hveravellir

Bárðarbunga and Holuhraun

Kerlingarfjöll

Þjórsárver

Landmannalaugar

Lakagígar and Skaftáreldahraun

Eldgjá

Hveravellir

Hveravellir is one of the more geologically powerful places in the highlands. It is located about 600 metres above sea level, between two of the country's largest ice-caps, Hofsjökull to the east and Langjökull to the west. At this elevation the vegetation is sparse, and the area looks rather barren. The Hveravellir hot spring area is not very large, but the springs are extremely varied, and on late-summer evenings they give the place a gloomy and almost ghostly air. The area's history is interesting. It sits midway between the north and south of the country, and for centuries it has been on a main thoroughfare. The area's most famous residents are undoubtedly the Icelandic outlaws, Fjalla-Eyvindur and Halla, who stayed there in the late 18th century. Remains of their dwelling can be seen just south of the hot spring area, and they cooked their food in one of the hot springs near to their hovel. A refuge hut has probably stood at Hveravellir for centuries, and in 1922 a new house was built on the foundations of an older one. In 1937 the Iceland Touring Association built a hut there, one of their three oldest mountain huts, so the area has been a tourist destination for a long time. The Hveravellir springs are vulnerable though, and the area must be treated well if it is to flourish as a future destination.

Hveravellir could be called the crown jewel of the highland region known as Kjölur, between Hofsjökull and Langjökull. Kjölur is bordered to the south by the rivers Hvítá and Jökulfall and to the north by Seyðisá and Svartakvísl. The area is very interesting because of the diverse geology, including many volcanic features, glaciers and glacial landforms, as well as a lovely spring area. To the east are large central volcanoes at Kerlingarfjöll and beneath Hofsjökull, and close to Hveravellir is the eastern edge of a third central volcano. It is usually named after the Þjófadalir valleys, but sometimes simply called the Hveravellir central volcano.

The Þjófadalir volcanic system is centred on the northern part of Langjökull, where the central volcano seems to be half-buried beneath the icecap. Unfortunately, the system has been studied very little. East of Hveravellir, just north of Þjófadalir, is the curved row of mountains called Þjófadalafjöll, and they are thought to be part of a caldera belonging to the central volcano beneath the icecap. Rhyolite is quite common in the mountains of Þjófadalafjöll. This is characteristic of a central volcano, and age-dating seems to suggest that the rhyolite is old, much of it around 500,000-700,000 years old. There have been a few eruptions in and around the Þjófadalir volcano since the end of the last glaciation (about 10,000 years ago), but most of them have been small, apart for the one that produced the Kjalhraun lava field about 8,000 years ago. The most recent eruption in the system was probably the one that formed Krákshraun, north on Stórisandur, and is thought to be about 4,500 years old.

Hveravellir is on the northern edge of Kjalhraun, directly north of the volcano that produced the lava. Kjalhraun formed in a large lava shield eruption, soon after the Ice Age glaciers had retreated from the country, and the volume of the lava is thought to have been 6-8 km^3. This makes it one of the largest lavas to be erupted after the end of glaciation. Kjalhraun is a good example of a very flat pahoehoe lava that was very runny when it was erupted. One of the characteristics of lava from a lava shield eruption like Kjalhraun, is that the magma involved is very hot. The high temperature, combined with the chemistry, means that the lava is runny and produces smooth-surfaced pahoehoe lava fields. This makes Kjalhraun easy to cross, and it is perfect to walk southwards from Hveravellir to Strýtur, the crater at the summit of the lava shield. The walk from Hveravellir to the crater is about five

or six kilometres long, and the lava shield slopes gently, so the total change in altitude is only about 200 m. Strýtur gets its name from some lovely lava pinnacles around the summit crater. The crater is about 500 m in diameter, making it a spectacular natural phenomenon.

Hveravellir is a high-temperature geothermal area, and a great variety of hot springs can be found there, with steaming fumaroles and mud pools. Exceptionally beautiful and diverse sinter formations have built up around the hot springs. Sinter is formed when dissolved solids in the hot spring water precipitate out as the water cools on the ground surface. The precipitations are mostly made of silica, and the silica content of the hot spring water at Hveravellir is among the highest found in Iceland. This explains the impressive sinter formations in the area, but the range of colours is also unusually large at Hveravellir. Among the well known springs in the area is fumarole Öskurhóll (Howling Hillock). It used to make a whistling sound, hence the name. Close by are Eyvindarhver and Rauðihver, and these three springs are among the oldest in the area. A little closer to the mountain huts are Bláhver and Grænihver, and the latter sometimes erupts in small spurts. On the other side of the footpath are two springs named Fagrihver and Meyjarauga, and they have both "stolen" their names because the names once belonged to other springs in the area. When older research on Hveravellir is studied, it can be seen that the hot spring area changes rapidly, and springs quicken and die fairly frequently. Names are transferred between springs when the older spring vanishes and a new one gains momentum. Most of the Hveravellir hot spring area is just north of the Kjalhraun lava field, but there is another hot spring area in the lava itself, which is worth looking at.

Kerlingarfjöll

Kerlingarfjöll is a majestic group of mountains in the central highlands, just south of Hofsjökull. The mountains are visible from many places in the southern lowlands as they stand isolated and higher than the surrounding highland plateau. For decades a ski school was operated there, from the early 1960s. It has been a while while since the ski lifts halted, and now tourist services are open over the summer, based in the old ski school. Kerling- arfjöll is probably one of the best-hidden highland gems, and the landscape and geology there concede little to Landmannalaugar or Hveravellir. Over the years, geoscientists have studied the mountains in some detail, both the volcano, the geothermal area in its centre, and the very small mountain glaciers found there. Despite this, there are many things still not understood about the geology and geological history of Kerlingarfjöll, and much research remains to be done.

Under the middle of the Kerlingarfjöll mountains is a large volcano, with many characteristics of a central volcano in its prime. Firstly, there is the enormous build-up of volcanic material, which, it is easy to imagine, occured quite rapidly at some point during the last glacial period. The high and magnificent peaks of Kerlingarfjöll are mainly made of rhyolite, a beautiful light-coloured rock type that many people know from Landmannalaugar, for example. One of the reasons for classing a particular area as a central volcano is that some of the rocks produced there are rhyolite or other "evolved" rocks, in contrast to the primitive basalt that is Iceland's most common rock type by far. Centrally in Kerlingarfjöll is a vast high-temperature geothermal area, yet another characteristic of central volcanoes in Iceland, and it is considered to be one of the most powerful geothermal areas in the country. Some of the highest surface temperatures have been measured there, about 145-150°C in steam vents at Hverabotn. Finally, there is the way in which the mountain group has built up. Kerlingarfjöll mountains

are usually divided into two areas, the western mountains which include Mænir, Höttur and Ögmundur, and the eastern mountains where Snækollur, Fannborg and Loðmundur tower. About 30 years ago it was first pointed out that parts of two calderas can be recognised in the mountains, one in the western mountains, and one in the eastern. Calderas are common in central volcanoes in Iceland. Askja, in the Dyngjufjöll mountain group, is probably best known, but there are also calderas at Grímsvötn, Katla and Krafla. Calderas are often thought to be formed in major eruptions during which the central volcano's magma chamber empties and the land subsequently subsides. The calderas at Kerlingarfjöll may have formed at the same time as the large rhyolite mountains, sometime in the Ice Age. However, they are now hard to see in the landscape because they have been half-filled by sediments and volcanic material.

One thing that is unclear regarding the Kerlingarfjöll central volcano is its connection with other volcanoes and its position regarding Iceland's volcanic belts. It has often been suggested that there is a connection between Kerlingarfjöll and the central volcano beneath Hofsjökull, and these two central volcanoes have even been called a single volcanic system. Any connection, however, is difficult to confirm because there is still a need for basic research on the two volcanoes. Also, geologists do not agree whether Kerlingarfjöll is an active volcano or not. The arguments for its active status include the high-temperature geothermal activity in the middle of the mountains, and their position on the edge of the active volcanic belt that crosses Iceland. On the other hand, the Kerlingarfjöll central volcano has not erupted since the end of glaciation. If it is still active, then it must be one of the country's least-active central volcanoes. Northeast of the Kerlingarfjöll mountains, between them and Hofsjökull, is one sign of postglacial volcanic activity in Kerlingarfjöll's neighbourhood. There lies the sand-covered Illahraun lava which probably actually formed in two eruptions, and which undoubtedly came from the Hofsjökull volcanic system, so it is not a sign of activity in the Kerlingarfjöll system. However, this lack of activity in the last thousands of years might not tell us everything, because the other two central volcanoes in the middle of the country, Hofsjökull and Tungnafellsjökull, have both been very quiet in postglacial times. These three volcanoes could be said to form a volcanically active fracture zone that might be called the Mid-Iceland Belt, connecting together the West Volcanic Zone in Langjökull and the East Volcanic Zone in Vatnajökull.

The Kerlingarfjöll central volcano has not been studied well enough to allow conclusions about its age. Based on mapping of the mountains and other landforms, it is obvious that most of them were formed subglacially, in a glacial period of the Ice Age – few lava formations from interglacial periods are found within the mountain group. It is, however, unclear when exactly the mountains were formed. The main peaks do not seem to have suffered from much glacial erosion, which suggests their young age. So perhaps the main period of eruptive activity in the volcano was during the last glaciation, about 10,000–130,000 years ago. However, age-dating that has been done on rocks from Kerlingarfjöll indicates that the mountains are much older than the last glacial period.

For geology enthusiasts, Kerlingarfjöll is practically paradise because few other places have such dynamic geology. Firstly, there are the many peaks, which offer almost endless possibilities for mountainous hiking trails. The peaks of Kerlingarfjöll clearly formed beneath an Ice Age glacier. Some eruptions reached the surface of the glacier and formed small tuyas (table mountains) with lava caps, and rhyolite tuyas like these are rare. Examples can be seen in the mountains Loðmundur and Hettur, where the lava caps give the mountains a particularly dignified appearance, while the other mountain peaks are more rounded. The highest peak in Kerlingarfjöll is Snækollur, 1488 m above sea level. It is said that in the

very best weather conditions it is possible to see all the way to both the north and south coasts, from the mountain's summit. In the middle of Kerlingarfjöll is the heart of the volcanic system, with a powerful high-temperature geothermal system and friable, colourful rhyolite patches. The high-temperature field in Kerlingarfjöll forms two or three separate areas. The largest area by far is called Neðri-Hveradalir and it is most popular with visitors, and most accessible. A vehicle track goes from the hut area at Ásgarður to the old ski area, and a side road to a car park lies just above the hot spring area. The lower part of Neðri-Hveradalir has clearly posted trails and paths that wind around gullies, stream beds and ridges, between boiling mud-pools and small glacier tongues. The Hveradalir area is very dynamic, and rapid changes can even be seen from year to year. On the slopes of Neðri-Hveradalir it is easy to see how the small glaciers are retreating in Kerling- arfjöll, and the water-logged slopes below the glaciers are constantly collapsing. The hot spring area also changes rapidly, and even large, powerful springs can disappear over a few years, while new ones form elsewhere. Only a few hot springs have been named, and best known is Snorrahver which lies below Hveradalahnúkur, highest in the Neðri-Hveradalir valley. The colours at Hveradalir are outstanding, and few places demonstrate the interplay of glaciers and hot springs so readily. Ice caves used to be accessible in the mountains, and they were a great attraction, but most, if not all, have now vanished.

Some distance above Neðri-Hveradalir, and further inside the central volcano's caldera, lies the Efri-Hveradalir area. This hot spring area is much smaller, and the springs lie along the south-eastern slopes of Snækollur. The third, and most remote spring area is in Hverabotn. It lies on the other side of Kerlingarskyggnir, west of Neðri-Hveradalir, so from Neðri-Hveradalir you have to work your way up the side of the glacier Langafönn to reach the area. It is quite a long walk from there over to Hverabotn, but the hot spring area is absolutely marvellous and just as stunning as alpine landscapes in other countries. Below Hverabotn is the desolate Sléttaskarð pass, surrounded by high rhyolite mountains on all sides. The hot spring areas in Kerlingarfjöll are exceptionally pristine, especially those in Efri-Hveradalir and Hverabotn, which are very remote. Consequently, it is important not to spoil the land by encroachment, and the fragile hot spring areas must be protected from trampling.

Like many other highland areas, Kerlingarfjöll has few ancient place names, and most names are relatively young. Þorvaldur Thoroddsen explored the area in the late 19th century, and named the mountain Ögmundur after his assistant. Visiting members of the Iceland Touring Association, and later the ski school, were diligent about adding names. The mountain group is itself named after a small móberg (hyaloclastite) pillar, Kerling or Old Lady, which lies in the west of the mountains, below Mt. Tindur. Kerlingarfjöll is a world-class natural gem. The landscape, with its high peaks and small mountain glaciers, is reminiscent of the Alps. The area is perfect for mountain activities of all sorts, skiing in winter and spring, or hiking in the summer. The mountains are still relatively little visited by tourists, and even if the flow increases it will still be possible to reach exceptional hot spring areas where hardly a soul is visible. For those who want to get even further away from the busiest areas and experience Kerlingarfjöll and the hot springs in total peace, all that is needed is to lace your hiking boots and set off.

Þjórsárver

Some readers may be unaware that there are six wetland areas in Iceland that are protected by international agreement. In 1971, the Ramsar Convention was adopted in the Iranian town of Ramsar, and there are now about 170 member countries (Contracting Parties). Participation commits Parties to nominate, be responsible for, and protect wetlands of international significance within their own borders. Iceland became a Contracting Party to the Ramsar Convention in 1978 when the area around Lake Mývatn and the Laxá river became the first Ramsar area in Iceland. Since then, five areas have been added to the list. Two of them are in Borgarfjörður, Andakíll and Grunnafjörður, and in the highlands there are three areas, the Snæfell-Eyjabakkar area, Guðlaugstungur and Þjórsárver.

A lot has been written and said about the ecosystem of Þjórsárver, and there is no need to repeat it here. The area is an extremely important tundra meadow, practically in the middle of the country. The ecosystem is unique, and Þjórsárver is one of the world's most important breeding grounds for the pink-footed goose. Þjórsárver was protected in 1981, but the area is not only important because of its ecosystem. The landscape is almost unparalleled anywhere in the world, lying lushly green with a coal-black desert on one side and one of Iceland's largest icecaps on the other. But how is it possible for such a green oasis to exist in the middle of Iceland's barren highlands?

Þjórsárver is a natural sedimentary basin, a depression in the bedrock which has been filled to a large extent by glacial river deposits. The depression is the result of several combined factors. Firstly, there is what could be called the "basic structure" of the country, as seen in the active volcanic belts. To the west is the West Volcanic Zone, with large central volcanoes at Kerlingarfjöll and Langjökull, and to the east

lies the East Volcanic Zone, with the high areas around the Tungnaá and Köldukvísl rivers – the source-area for some of the largest lava eruptions on Earth since the end of glaciation. To the north is the enormous volcano beneath Hofsjökull, with an ice-filled caldera in the middle of the ice-cap, one of the largest calderas in Iceland. There has been considerable accumulation of volcanic material in all these areas since the end of glaciation, while the bedrock at Þjórsárver has been left out, and the youngest rock there is thought to be about 500,000 years old. Relative to the build-up of the land in the volcanic belts, Þjórsárver is a passive depression with active volcanic belts on three sides. A few postglacial lavas associated with the Hofsjökull volcano have been erupted onto the margins of the area, but they are small and have barely touched Þjórsárver itself.

During the Ice Age, glacial ice enslaved the whole country, and it contributed to the deepening of the Þjórsárver basin. Ice Age glacial landforms can be seen widely-scratched and striated rocks, moraines, and drumlins. These features tell us the history of the Ice Age glacier at each location, how the ice flowed across the landscape and how the glacier retreated when glaciation ended. Icelandic geologist Guðmundur Kjartansson did pioneering research in the mid 20th century on glacial striations in Iceland. Striations are scratches in the bedrock, made by moving glaciers. Guðmundur Kjartansson studied glacial landforms in the highlands, especially south of the icecaps, and in the middle of the century he set out important ideas about the position and movement of the Ice Age glacier. He pointed out that the main direction of glacial striations in the highlands south of Hofsjökull and Sprengisandur was towards the northwest, and not the southeast as might have been expected. From this, Guðmundur concluded that the Ice Age glacier had been thickest in the Tungnaá area, southeast of Þjórsárver, and it had flowed towards the west and northwest, across the basin. The middle of Iceland's ice-sheet was, in fact, not in the centre of the country, rather it was quite some distance south of the current watershed on Sprengisandur and Kjölur.

In the latter half of the 20th century, the retreat of the ice-sheet from the central highlands was studied further, and the research indicated that when glaciation peaked, around 25,000 years ago, the ice-sheet was centred on the central highlands. Ancient glacial striations with a southwest direction can be found in the region, indicating that the ice-sheet flowed southwest across the Þjórsárver basin. After the peak of glaciation, the ice-sheet thinned quite rapidly and its flow direction changed. Its centre shifted to the Tungnaá highland area, and from there it flowed northwest over the Þjórsárver area. Irrespective of whether the centre of the ice-sheet lay in the middle of the country or a little south of Hofsjökull at the peak of glaciation, geologists generally agree that after it reached its maximum, the glacier retreated into the Tungnaá area, where it remained longer than in most other places. At this time, the glacier lay on the southeast margin of Þjórsárver, and glacial tongues stretched to the northwest, across the path of the current Þjórsá river. The glacier dammed drainage from the highlands towards the south, and created a glacial lake at Þjórsárver. While the glacial lake covered the area, a large quantity of sand and gravel was carried into the lake by glacial rivers, and lake sediments were deposited, almost filling the lake.

Over time the glacier retreated further to the southeast, and the lake's surface fell in a few steps. At first the lake surface was at about 670 m above sea level. It fell to 640 m, 585–590 m, and finally 575 m above sea level. One lake remained after

the glacier had vanished from the area, and the river Þjórsá probably flowed from the lake, south to Norðlingaalda. This lake gradually filled with river sediments, like its predecessor, but finally the Þjórsá eroded down through a natural rock dam south of Norðlingaalda, where it now flows, so the lake emptied. The upper part of the Þjórsá has a very shallow gradient, and this has played its part in creating a high water table in the region. Many of the streams feeding the Þjórsá originate by glacier snouts at around 620-640 m above sea level, but 15-25 km downstream, at Sóleyjarhöfði, the channel has only dropped to an altitude of 570-580 m.

In the thousands of years following the end of glaciation, Þjórsárver became vegetated, and signs of a strong plant community from this time are widespread. However, in the cooling climate of the last thousand years the vegetation has declined, and it is now largely limited to flat wetland areas – the *ver* of the place name. These areas are usually located where the old glacial lakes stood; the ground is impermeable, and the water table is high there. In these areas palsa mires form. These are areas of permafrost, ground containing ice all year round. Permafrost areas are widespread in the highlands, but the largest ones are at Þjórsárver. The palsa mires are characterised by a landscape of low circular or oval mounds called palsas, and which contain cores of ice. The growing ice cores push the overlying ground upwards, forming mounds. The mounds can rise up to 1.5 m, and the largest ones are a few metres long. Over time, the surface of a palsa cracks and fissures extend down to the frozen ground, allowing thawing so that the mound disappears.

It is obvious from all of this that the geological environment at Þjórsárver is unique, and it plays a large part in creating this remarkable habitat. But Þjórsárver is not the only special area, and north of Hofsjökull are two other unusual areas, Guðlaugstungur and Orravatnsrústir. The conservation value of the countryside around Hofsjökull can be said to be very high, both in regard to the biota and geological formations, and not least because it is a pristine landscape unit. The greatest disruption in the vicinity of Hofsjökull is due to the Kvíslaveita hydro-scheme – part of Þjórsárver was flooded, and flow in Þjórsá downstream from the vegetated area was considerably curtailed. Disregarding Kvíslaveita, the area is free from any power schemes or large constructions. It would therefore be natural to aim at establishing a national park at Hofsjökull, to protect the central highlands and give it the status that it deserves. In the south, the national park would need to include Þjórsárver and the Þjórsá river channel to below Gljúfurleitarfoss, along with the Kerlingarfjöll mountains. To the north, it should include Guðlaugstungur, as far as Hofsafrétt, past Ásbjarnarvötn and Orravatnsrústir, and east to Laugafell. The Hofsjökull national park would include three of the most important palsa and permafrost areas in the country – their biota is of global significance. Protection of the Hofsjökull area is thus a golden opportunity to protect one of the most remarkable parts of Iceland's highlands, and in time it might be possible to combine it with Vatnajökull National Park, making one continuous Highland Park. Two things threaten these areas in particular. One is the unending planned extension of hydropower production schemes, such as Norðlingaölduveita and the harnessing of glacial rivers in Skagafjörður. The other threat is the plan to install a high-voltage electricity line along the Sprengisandur route. Every effort must be made to resist these plans – it is our responsibility to protect and nurture this globally significant region.

Landmannalaugar

Landmannalaugar is among the most popular destinations in Iceland's highlands, and one of the most photographed. The area around Landmannalaugar is one of the most varied and colourful in the highlands and should leave no one unmoved. On sunny summer days, the campsite next to the Iceland Touring Association's mountain huts is thronged with people, and some complain that it is too crowded in peak season. It is, however, easy to get away from the crowds, simply by following one of the amazing hiking trails in the neighbourhood. Just beyond the campsite, it is as though nature completely swallows the tourists, and the peace of the wilderness returns.

The Landmannalaugar area is known for its varied geology, but when it comes to understanding the geological history of the area, things get tricky because the geology is very complicated. Volcanic activity around Landmannalaugar is linked to a large central volcano named after Torfajökull, although the icecap and its underlying mountain are in fact only a small part of the volcano. The Torfajökull volcano has been active for a fairly long time. The oldest age-dated rocks in the volcano are about 400,000 years old, but the oldest geological formations are thought to be up to twice as old. During its lifetime, the volcano has managed to produce one of Iceland's largest areas of rhyolite rock, and it is not done yet – there have been two eruptions since Iceland's settlement, and Iceland's largest, and one of Iceland's largest and most powerful high-temperature geothermal areas is there. As is common in evolved central vol-

canoes like the one at Torfajökull, different fragments of the volcano are mixed together like an enormous pot of porridge, so it can be difficult to recognise formations of different ages. It has consequently required a lot of research and study to unravel the situation, and this work is far from finished because much remains unclear. However, in 2001, an excellent summary report about the geology of the Torfajökull system was published, based on tireless work by numerous Icelandic and international geologists. To appreciate the complexity of the geological research in the area, it is possible to look at the geological map in the report – it is practically incomprehensible to any but the most resolute geologists.

The geology of the Torfajökull volcano is not only complicated, it is also very interesting. For most of its lifetime it erupted almost only rhyolite, which is unusual for an Icelandic central volcano. Basaltic eruptions did not occur until the last glacial period, and rhyolite has continued to be erupted in the middle of the volcano, as can be seen by the youngest lavas. In the centre of the Torfajökull volcano hides Iceland's largest caldera formation. A central volcano caldera is a type of graben or valley, formed by major subsidence, often following a big eruption. Geologists first recognised the existence and size of the Torfajökull caldera in around 1970. The slightly elongated, curving caldera stretches from Torfajökull in the southeast, westwards to Reykjadalir, where the uppermost source of the Markarfljót river lies. In fact, there are three calderas of different ages, which crosscut each other to some degree, but the outermost caldera is oldest, and it can also be seen most easily in the landscape. The southern rim of that caldera lies through Ljósárfjöll and Jökultungur, where the Laugavegur hiking trail descends to Lake Álftavatn, while the northern rim lies along the curved mountain range outside Landmannalaugar, through Hábarmur, Barmur and Suðurnámur.

At Landmannalaugar, sharp contrasts in the landscape meet. The glorious colour of the surrounding mountains is unusual, and various shades of yellow, red, blue and green can be seen. At the hot spring area, the jet-black and rough lava that guards the area is no less eye catching. It is the Laugahraun lava, erupted in a short fissure eruption in 1477 – the same eruption series that produced the enormous flood of lava at Veiðivötn, northeast of Landmannalaugar. The lava is the most recent product of the Torfajökull region, and since the previously mentioned caldera-rim mountains Barmur and Suðurnámur are just north of Landmannalaugar, it can be said that the youngest and oldest parts of the Torfajökull volcano meet there. Laugahraun is a rhyolite lava, one of the few to be erupted after Iceland's settlement. The lava field is very thick and rough, making it difficult to cross. The lava was obviously very viscous when it was erupted. Rhyolite is usually much more viscous than basalt lava, both because of its chemical composition and because rhyolite magma is usually erupted at a lower temperature. As evidence of this, the Laugahraun vents can barely be seen because the viscous lava has been unable to flow away from them, so it has accumulated on the craters instead. One of the loveliest parts of Laugahraun is just above Landmannalaugar, where the eruptive fissure lies along Brennisteinsalda, a colourful rhyolite mountain that formed in a subglacial eruption a few hundred thousand years ago. The lava there has semi-leaked down the hillside and the jet-black formations contrast with the multitude of colours on Brennisteinsalda. The colours of Brennisteinsalda, like other mountains in the area, have been produced by the high temperatures that have hydrothermally altered it over a long time.

One of the most unusual things about the youngest lavas in the Torfajökull area, like Laugahraun, is that they are all linked to volcanic events in the southern part of the Bárðarbunga volcanic system, which is northeast of Landmannalaugar. The eruption at Veiðivötn happened at the same time as Laugahraun was formed, and about 500 years earlier the Hrafntinnuhraun lava, west of Mt. Hrafntinnusker, was produced in an eruption at the same time as the Vatnaalda eruption, northeast of Landmannalaugar. These eruptions were all along fissures extending from the Bárðarbunga volcanic system. The total volume of eruptive material is less than it used to be earlier in the Torfajökull volcano's history, when there used to be regular large eruptions. These things all indicate that the Torfajökull area is now less active as an independent volcanic system, but beneath it is some rhyolite magma which reacts to activity in neighbouring systems. When the Bárðarbunga system sent magma towards the southwest, it appears to have triggered an eruption in the Torfajökull volcano.

The mountains behind Landmannalaugar are beautiful to look at, but many people want to enjoy the view from the top as well. Háalda is one of the higher mountains at Landmannalaugar and an excellent viewpoint. It formed in an eruption beneath a glacier at about the same time as Brennisteinsalda. Close to the hot spring area is Bláhnúkur, probably the area's most popular mountain to climb. To get there, it is easiest to hike round the Laugahraun lava field to Grænagil, and then across the Brennisteinsöldukvísl stream, to the foot of the mountain. It is also excellent to make a circle and hike up the Grænagil gully to the foot of Bláhnúkur, opposite Brennisteinsalda, and then up the mountain. Bláhnúkur stands out in the mountains around Landmannalaugar because it is dark grey in colour, even though it is a rhyolite mountain like the others. It formed much later though, beneath a glacier about 70,000-

80,000 years ago, and the rock has not been altered in the same way as other places. However, on the slopes of Bláhnúkur, it is possible to glimpse pale rhyolite which was already there when it erupted, and in Grænagil the rock has been totally altered by hydrothermal activity, so that it has taken on a deep green colour. This suggests that the rock used to be quite deep in the earth where high temperatures prevailed, and in many other places in the Torfajökull area a green sheen can be seen on the rock, indicating the high temperatures existing there.

Like many other natural highland gems, a large part of the experience of visiting Landmannalaugar is the journey to get there. It is possible to drive to Landmannalaugar along three beautiful highland roads, each with its own attractions, and they are usually referred to as Fjallabaksleið nyrðri. It is easiest to leave from Sigalda as there are no rivers to ford on that route. There are small rivers on the way through Dómadalur and east from Hólaskjól, but they

should be passable for small 4x4s unless the rivers are in flood. From the east, Fjallabaksleið goes through Eldgjá, among other places, and approaching from the west the route goes past Ljótipollur which formed in the great Veiðivötn eruption in 1477, at the same time as Laugahraun was erupted. All these routes meet close to Landmannalaugar, and the last part of the drive is across a lava tongue named Námshraun. It was also erupted in 1477. Then the route goes into the caldera rim, along Jökulgilskvísl, one source of which is the Torfajökull glacier. As the destination is reached, a vista opens across the grassy spring area of Landmannalaugar. Two rivers have to be crossed, Námskvísl and a small stream which is sometimes called Laugakvísl. Travellers in smaller vehicles should stop here, in the car park before the ford. From there it is a short walk to the paradise of Landmannalaugar, where the Iceland Touring Association erected their first mountain hut in 1951, although the oldest part of the current hut is from 1969.

Eldgjá

The highland region between the Mýrdals-jökull and Vatnajökull icecaps is one of the most volcanically active areas in Iceland. Eruptions may not be as frequent as in many other areas, but when eruptions do occur they are like no other. This was proved in the Laki eruption late in the 18th century, when the lowland area was almost drowned in lava and glowing ash. The first inhabitants of Iceland were also able to experience this. Immediately after the first settlers arrived, there was an eruption in a remote highland region called Vatnsöldur, from which Landnámslag can be traced – a layer of ash found widely in Iceland and with an age corresponding to the settlement period. The first major eruption in the area after this, with lava flows down to the rural lowlands, was only about 60 years after Iceland's settlement began. It is thought to have been in 934 that the ground ripped apart along a roughly 60 km long fissure, now called Eldgjá, or the Fire Fissure. In spite of its size, little was known about the eruption – there are no contemporary accounts of it, and the historical records are fairly quiet on the subject, although some people think that accounts in Landnámabók, the book of settlement, can be connected to the eruption. However, in recent years the eruption has been studied a lot, and it is now thought that it was the most voluminous basalt eruption on Earth during that period of history.

The first geologist to see Eldgjá was the Icelandic geologist Þorvaldur Thoroddsen, in the summer of 1893. He described Eldgjá in broad outline in his travel journals, and he was first to introduce Eldgjá to the scientific world, even though local people from the Skaftafell district were well acquainted with the fissure. After Þorvaldur's description was published, quite a lot was written about Eldgjá and its geology, but it was not until recent decades that any real progress has been made regarding this enormous eruption. Around 1980 it was demonstrated that the lava and rootless cones in the Álftaver area, as well as the Landbrotshraun lava south of Kirkjubæjarklaustur, came from Eldgjá – they are all of a similar age, and

this view has been widely accepted. Many people have estimated the surface area of the Eldgjá lava, and it is now thought to be about 840 km^2 in area, although a large part of it is covered by the younger Laki lava and, on the Mýrdalssandur plain, flood deposits from Katla's glacial floods. Its volume is even less certain, and numbers from 15 up to 19 km^3 have been mentioned. In recent years the effect of the Eldgjá eruption on the early Icelandic population has been studied further, and the global impact of the eruption has been studied too - a vast quantity of volcanic material and gases were expelled in the eruption. It is now thought that this had a great effect on climate around the world and even reduced the strength of the monsoon wind, causing long-term drought in the Nile region of Egypt.

It is not completely clear how the eruption proceeded. However, most agree that Eldgjá was formed in a single eruption or eruptive episode, and that the activity began in 934. The date was determined by studying volcanic ash in ice-cores from the Greenland icecap, but historical records from other countries also mention changes in weather conditions that can be linked to the eruption. Unlike the Laki eruption which lasted for only eight months, the Eldgjá eruption probably lasted for a few years, possibly until after 940. So the total activity was spread over quite a long time, with a few periods of immense explosive activity and quiet periods between. It is now believed that at least 18 km^3 of lava poured out in the eruption, and 1-5 km^3 of ash. The total volume of erupted materials is therefore over 20 km^3, considerably more than in the Laki eruption. The Eldgjá fissure stretches about 57 km towards the northeast, from the northeast corner of the Mýrdalsjökull icecap. At the margin of the icecap, the fissure vanishes under the glacier, where an enormous explosive eruption has taken place, under the ice. This is demonstrated by the big ash fall which has been traced to this part of the fissure, and this explosive event is considered to mark the start of the eruption. Moving away from the glacier, the fissure is rather disjointed, so it is quite a distance between its different parts. Probably the volcanic activity moved in bursts ever further from the icecap, so it never erupted along the whole fissure at the same time. Research has shown that at some places there are up to eight different layers of tephra (ash and coarser particles) from the Eldgjá eruption, and from this it is concluded that the eruption consisted of at least eight separate events.

Another important part of research into Eldgjá and the Eldgjá lavas, is to examine the origin of the magma that was erupted. The Eldgjá lavas are chemically very similar to lava and other volcanic material from the Katla volcano under Mýrdalsjökull, and based on this, it has been suggested that the magma which erupted in the Eldgjá eruption originated in the Katla volcanic system. This is a similar relationship to that of the Laki eruption and Grímsvötn volcano. Many people believe that during the eruption, the Eldgjá fissure extended all the way to Katla's caldera, so it was about 75 km long. It is fairly certain that Katla erupted at a similar time to the Eldgjá eruption, supporting the theory that a sudden intrusion of magma occurred. If that is the case, then an enormous volume of magma was pushed out from Katla's magma cham-ber, along the fissure system towards the northeast. There, the magma reached the surface along the Eldgjá fissure.

Based on geological mapping, the Eldgjá fissure can be divided into three parts along its length: western, middle and eastern sections. The western section lies under the Mýrdalsjökull icecap, and the most eastern section is only about five kilometres from Vatnajökull, so the eruption nearly reached from icecap to icecap. The western section of the Eldgjá fissure lies from Mýrdalsjökull to the river Hólmsá, and two narrow lava streams lead from it, down to the lowland. There they form the lava field at Álftaver and extend to the sea at the cliffs called Alviðruhamrar. The middle section of the fissure is in two parts. The western half is almost ten kilometres long, and lava from it flowed along what is now the Syðri-Ófæra river channel, down to the lowland. The eastern half is the best-known part of the Eldgjá fissure, the part that most people mean when they say "Eldgjá", and it is about eight kilometres long. Access to the fissure is best there, with the mountain road Fjallabaksleið nyrðri (F208) close by. From the road there is a short track to the car park at Nyrðri-Ófæra, in the middle of the canyon. From there it is easy to walk to the beautiful Ófærufoss, a three-tiered waterfall. Above the lower tier

of the waterfall there used to be a majestic rock arch over the river, but it collapsed in 1993.

The Eldgjá fissure is most impressive on the way to Ófærufoss. Just after the waterfall, the fissure is about 500 m wide from edge to edge, and up to 140 m deep. The sides of fissure are mainly made of móberg (hyaloclastite) and glacial tillite. This is seen best in the fissure walls by Ófærufoss. Uppermost in the walls of the fissure, thick layers of lava can be seen – tens of metres thick in some places. Visitors might think that the lava was erupted from the fissure, but this cannot be correct because it is believed that lava did not flow over the edges. The layers of lava were actually formed by the fusing together of lava droplets, splashes from lava fountains. So they are evidence of the tremendous lava fountain activity – lava would have been sprayed hundreds of metres up from the fissure. The main lava from this part of the Eldgjá fissure flowed down to the lowland through a mountain gap where the road Fjallabaksleið nyrðri now lies. Lavas from the middle section of the fissure are very extensive. However, to a large extent they are covered by the Eldhraun lava from the Laki fissure, so we only see part of the original lavas. They peep out from under the Eldhraun lava in places though – southwest of the Eldhraun lava field, on the eastern bank of the Kúðafljót river, and also east of it, where the particularly beautiful Land-brotshólar indicate their presence. Land-brotshólar are rootless cones, formed when lava from Eldgjá flowed over wetlands. They form the largest continuous area of rootless cones in the country. The northern section of the Eldgjá fissure consists of crater rows, including the Kambagígur crater, just north of the Laki crater row.

From geological research it is clear that the effects of the Eldgjá eruption must have been severe for the early settlers of Iceland. The eruption was enormous, and the flood of lava terrible for pioneer farmsteads in southeast Iceland. Total sulphur emissions from the eruption were probably the highest from any eruption in the last thousand years, and almost double the emissions from the Laki craters. However, in all likelihood, activity was spread over a few years, so it is not certain that the consequences were as dramatic as those following Laki, although they must have been very protracted. Now, about a thousand years later, we are free to admire the fantastic beauty of the massive volcanic fissure. But, in light of the devastation that the eruption caused, it is appropriate to treat Eldgjá with respect and humility.

Lakagígar and Skaftáreldahraun

Since the first settlers arrived in Iceland no event has had such as deep and lasting effect on human life as the 1783-1784 eruption at Lakagígar, the Laki crater row. In addition to the lava, which flooded over the countryside and destroyed farms and meadows, volcanic ash and polluting gases were spread across the land. The events lay heavily on Icelanders, and in the period from 1783 until 1786 the population fell by almost 20%, from 50,000 people to just below 40,000. The Laki eruption and its associated events can hardly be held solely responsible for the loss of life – the weather was exceptionally unfavourable and a series of major earthquakes in south Iceland, as well as a smallpox epidemic, afflicted the country during these years. However, the eruption has always been seen as the underlying cause of the largest population decrease in the history of Iceland. In Icelandic the eruption and lava flow are usually both named after the local river and called Skaftáreldar (Skaftá Fires)

and Skaftáreldahraun, but the devastation that followed is known best as móðuharðindin – the hardship of the haze, after the volcanic gases which were erupted.

The Laki crater row eruption began early in June 1783, and it was to last for seven or eight months. There are various reports of the volcanic activity, but the best are the three descriptions by Jón Steingrímsson, pastor at Prestbakki in the Síða district. His are the only eye witness accounts of the volcanic activity, and his descriptions of the eruption and human tragedy are riveting. In the days preceding the eruption, earthquakes had been felt in the farming district, and people had even decided to sleep outdoors in tents because of them. On Whit Sunday, 8 June, a cloud of ash suddenly appeared over the highlands. The cloud drifted over the farming district on the lowlands, and immediately there was a large fall of ash. This would continue while the eruption lasted. Inhabitants in the district

could soon see eruption columns above the volcanic fissure in the highlands – lava fountains in the Laki eruption are thought to have reached 800–1400 m high. News came too of lava flowing rapidly down the Skaftá river channel. On 12 June lava flowed onto the lowland for the first time, from the mouth of the Skaftá river canyon. The river itself had ceased to flow some time previously. Thin-flowing lava poured from the canyon, over the district's meadows and fields below, and in the following weeks many farms ended under the lava, and others were ruined by ash and cinders. Down on the lowlands, the lava followed the three channels of the Skaftá river and spread out steadily. One branch poured straight from the canyon down towards the sea and flowed over older lava that had come from the Eldgjá eruption in the 10th century. That branch halted in the second half of June,

but the other two, which lay west and east of the canyon, flowed for a longer time. The eastern branch ran along the Skaftá riverbed and headed rapidly along the narrow channel towards Kirkjubæjar- klaustur, posing a great threat. Sunday 20 July, Pastor Jón Steingrímsson held a church service at Klaustur, in such intense heat and mist from the lava that it was barely possible to see through the vapour. Many were convinced that it would be the last Sunday service in the church – the lava flow was almost there. At the end of the service, the church guests walked out and saw that the lava tongue had stopped just above the church, less than a kilometre from the crag Systrastapi. It has since been called the Fire Sermon Point, and Pastor Jón Steingrímsson was given the nickname Fire Cleric because of his performance. This marked the maximum extent of the lava along the

Skaftá, and soon afterwards water began to flow down the river channel again. The Skaftá canyon was full of lava by then, but the eruption had not ended although it was a lot less forceful.

On 29 July the roar of eruption was heard again from the crater area, but this time the location was further north than before. In early August the river Hverfisfljót dried up, and on 7 August the lava poured out of its river canyon. This eastern branch of the lava soon surrounded the Orrustuhóll islet, destroying a few farms in the Fljóts-hverfi district on the way. After that, a number of surges of lava came down the Hverf-isfljót channel in August and September. Finally, thin-flowing lava came down the eastern channel late in October. Eruptions on the Laki crater row are thought to have continued until February 1784.

The Laki crater row was examined by natural scientists immediately after the eruption, and has since been described by many geologists. Accurate mapping of the volcanic vents and lavas took place in the 1980s, with the help of aerial photographs. There are 135-140 Laki craters in total that erupted along a 27 km long fissure, running southwest-northeast. The craters were formed in mixed eruptions of lava and tephra, and most of them are spatter cones, formed from semi-molten lava splashes. In between them are some scoria cones, as well as two beautifully formed ash cones. As the description of the lava flows in the farming region indicates, volcanic activity occurred in two main phases, but the eruption has been divided into a total of ten separate episodes. First the southern part of the fissure erupted, south of Mt. Laki, and lava flowed down the Skaftá river channel and formed the Eldhraun lava field. In July the main activity moved to the northern part of the fissure, and the lava poured down the Hverfisfljót channel, where it is called Brunahraun. The flow rate in the first two eruptive episodes was about 5000-6600 m^3/s, which is about fifteen times the average flow rate in Iceland's biggest river, the Ölfusá. It is no wonder, therefore, that the local people were terrified when the flood of lava hit the lowlands.

In the end, lava from the Laki craters covered an area of 580-600 km^2, which is 0.5% of the whole country. For a long time, the volume of lava and ash was estimated to be 12 km^3, but this figure is uncertain because it is difficult to determine the thickness of the lava, or the underlying landscape. Geologists have since suggested other estimates ranging from 10.4 to 14.7 km^3. Irrespective of the exact figure, it is obvious that the Laki fissure eruption was the second-largest lava eruption on Earth during this period, after the Eldgjá eruption of 934. The volume of magma was enormous, but its chemical composition does not indicate that it came directly from the mantle; instead, the magma seems to have paused in a magma chamber on its way up. Most people now think that the Laki eruption was connected to the Grímsvötn central volcano in the Vatnajökull icecap, and that the lava which erupted in the Laki crater row originated there – it is very similar to magma from Grímsvötn. In addition, volcanic activity was going on at Grímsvötn while the Laki eruption took place, and that strongly indicates a connection between them

The "hardship of the haze" was attributed to air pollution that accompanied the eruption. In addition to lava and ash, considerable quantities of gases can be erupted by volcanoes. When magma is carried upwards through the earth's crust, in the prelude to an eruption, it is rich in gases like water vapour, sulphur and carbon dioxide, but also contains minor amounts of other gases, such as chlorine and fluorine. These gases are dissolved in the magma when it is at great depths, but they are released when the pressure falls during the eruption – just as carbon dioxide is released from a bottle of soda when the top is unscrewed. Because they have different properties, the gases are not all released from the magma at the same time. Most of them are released immediately in the eruption and are carried with the eruption cloud The gases that go through this are mainly water vapour, carbon dioxide and sulphur. However, quite a lot of gas remains in the lava after it begins to flow, and in the case of the Laki eruption, sulphur, fluorine and chlorine compounds were all released from the lava, both while it was flowing, and after it solidified. After being released from the lava, these compounds underwent condensation and formed small mist particles, creating a bluish haze in the atmosphere. Because the Laki lavas flowed for both a long time and over a large area, the pollution in the nearby area was severe. It was caused by sulphur emissions as well as fluorine and chlorine pollution; such compounds are usually quite toxic and cause diseases in livestock. The weather conditions in the area did not help either – Kirkjubæjarklaustur is usually quite calm, and wind conditions at the eruption site carried the pollution westwards over the highlands to the southern uplands, and to the north of the country.

Most well equipped 4x4 vehicles can get to the Laki crater area and it is possible to drive a circular route around the area. Please note that the Laki crater row is a protected area and part of Vatnajökull National Park, so the area must be treated with respect. The craters are fragile and covered with delicate moss, so walking is only permitted on the paths and marked trails. There are lovely trails up Mt. Laki, with a panoramic view from the top, and also around Tjarnagígur, one of the craters. There is a campsite at Blágil, just outside the National Park boundary.

Bárðarbunga and Holuhraun

This chapter about Bárðarbunga and Holuhraun covers one of the most recent events in the geology of Iceland, and it started in the second half of 2014. At the beginning of August, earthquake activity suddenly increased in the Bárðarbunga volcano, and an eruption started at Holuhraun less than a month later. The eruption was very prolonged and ended six months later, on 27 February 2015. These events were some of the most remarkable of the last couple of years, and it is not clear if they have actually come to an end. Consequently, this chapter could become rapidly obsolete, so bear that in mind.

Bárðarbunga is one of Iceland's most active central volcanoes, at the heart of a volcanic system that usually carries the same name, although it is also known as the Veiðivötn system. Briefly, a central volcano is a volcano that has erupted repeatedly in the same area over a long geological period. This results in a large volcano or group of mountains, often accompanied by geother-

mal activity and the production of rhyolite. There is little sign of Bárðarbunga on the surface because it is hidden by a thick icecap, but if the glacier was stripped from the land, a large group of mountains would be revealed, rising to 1850 m above sea level and about 800-900 m above its surroundings. In the middle of the volcano is a 500-600 m deep circular graben or caldera, one of the largest in Iceland, and the glacier inside the caldera is up to 800 m thick. Near to Bárðarbunga are two other very active central volcanoes beneath the same icecap, Grímsvötn and Kverkfjöll. Together, these volcanoes sit on the most active part of the country, the middle of the Iceland hotspot, beneath which is a mantle plume where unusually hot mantle material is brought up under the earth's crust. This is the cause of the great volcanic activity.

The Bárðarbunga volcanic system is one of the two largest volcanic systems in Iceland and stretches over a 190-km-long

area of land, all the way from the Torfajökull caldera, northeast under Vatnajökull and then continuing north to Dyngjufjöll, where it meets the Askja volcanic system. In this region are many large móberg (hyaloclastite) formations which were erupted during the Ice Age, and also vast areas of lava which flowed after the Ice Age glacier had vanished. It is good to keep in mind that the outer limits of the volcanic system have simply been drawn around the recent volcanic features and faults that are thought to be linked to Bárðarbunga, or that have some clear connection to it. Demarcation of the volcanic system is based on visible signs of volcanic activity and tectonic rifting, and the extent of individual volcanic systems as drawn on a map should not be taken too literally. Geoscientists' understanding of volcanic activity in Iceland changes remarkably rapidly – modern geology is a younger subject than many people suspect, and we are a long way from understanding things entirely,, as became obvious during the Holuhraun eruption.

The central volcanoes beneath the northwestern part of Vatnajökull were all virtually unknown until well into the 20th century. Research expeditions in the first half of the century improved the situation greatly, especially for Grímsvötn – the most powerful volcano beneath Vatnajökull. The nature and extent of the Bárðarbunga volcano, however, was not well known until the 1970s when studies got underway. In 1973 NASA's new satellite took a series of very interesting photographs of Vatnajökull, and the shapes of various hitherto unknown land forms beneath the ice could be recognised, including a vast ice-filled caldera at the top of Bárðarbunga. A few years later, radio-echo sounding methods were first used in the northwest part of Vatnajökull. Measurements of the base of the icecap were made, confirming the existence of the

caldera. Continued radio-echo sounding investigations in the 1970s and -80s stripped the icecap of its mystery and revealed three large central volcanoes, along with smaller volcanoes. Between them were deep, wide valleys. The dramatic landscape beneath the glacier is not revealed at all on the surface of the icecap, which is smooth and gently sloping in most places, indicating that the ice is of quite varied thickness. The glacier is about 200–400 m thick on the south and east sides of Bárðarbunga, and even thinner on the northwest side, while the ice is up to 850 m thick in the Bárðarbunga caldera. In the valley between Bárðarbunga and Grímsvötn, where the volcano Gjálp erupted in 1996, the glacier is up to 700 m thick, and it is even thicker in the valley between Bárðarbunga and Kverkfjöll. This knowledge of the icecap is extremely important for volcanic research in Vatnajökull – it makes a lot of difference to ice melting and the size of outburst floods if the eruption is beneath thick or thin areas of glacier.

In the last decade, knowledge of Bárðarbunga, and its volcanic system, has increased rapidly, and now it is obvious that the most recent events are only the latest in a long history of activity. Bárðarbunga volcano has erupted persistently, with over 20 subglacial eruptions since Iceland was settled, and since the end of glaciation, about 11,000 years ago, there must have been hundreds of eruptions, even though knowledge of them is limited. A fairly powerful series of eruptions seems to have taken place in around 1700, with large outburst floods down the Jökulsá á Fjöllum river channel. The greatest eruptions in the Bárðarbunga volcanic system do not occur in the central volcano itself; instead they occur on eruptive fissures outside of the icecap. Since the end of glaciation, there have been 30 eruptions in the Veiðivötn region and north of Vatnajökull, close to Trölladyngja. The largest of these, and one of the largest post-glacial lava eruptions anywhere on Earth, was in the Veiðivötn highlands about 8600 years ago when the great Þjórsárhraun lava flowed more than 130 km, down to the coast between the rivers Þjórsá and Ölfusá.

Since settlement times, there have been four large explosive eruptions in the Bárðarbunga volcanic system, as well as the new eruption at Holuhraun. The first eruption was at Vatnaöldur, southwest of Vatnajökull, and the eruptive fissure stretched over 60 km, from Vatnajökull and south of the Torfajökull area. Because of the high water table at the eruption site, little or no lava flowed; instead, the magma was shattered and became ash that spread over most of the country. Unique to this eruption, the magma from Bárðarbunga pushed its way through the Torfajökull area and also erupted southwest of it. At the same time, Bárðarbunga probably triggered an eruption in the Torfajökull volcanic system. In the eruption at Torfajökull, rhyolite magma was erupted, and ash from this eruption is light-coloured and lies directly on top of black ash from Vatnaöldur. The ash layer is beautifully double-layered, pale above and dark below, and distinctive where it occurs in the soil profile. It has long been known that the eruption at Vatnaöldur occurred at about the same time as Iceland was settled, and this distinctive layer has been called Landnámslagið - the Settlement Layer. It has proved very useful for determining the age of archaeological remains from Iceland's early human history. In 1995, signs of the ash layer were recognised in ice cores from Greenland, and based on this it was possible to determine a date for the eruption with only a two-year margin of error. The ash fell in 871.

There was another eruption in the Bárðarbunga system at Frambruni, north of Vatnajökull, probably in the 13th century, and in 1477 an enormous tephra eruption occurred in the southwest area. The Veiðivötn crater row formed then, on a 60–65 km long eruptive fissure, and again the activity provoked the Torfajökull area and two rhyolite lavas were erupted at Landmannalaugar - Laugahraun and Námshraun. The last eruption in Bárðarbunga, until the most recent one, occurred at the margin of Sylgjujökull glacier, southwest of Bárðarbunga in 1862-64, when the Tröllahraun lava was erupted. The interesting thing about that eruption is its length, and also the severe and long-lasting volcanic haze which accompanied it, similar to what occurred during the Holuhraun eruption in 2014-15. After the Tröllahraun eruption, Bárðarbunga may have erupted, again in 1902 or 1910, but after that, all was quiet until after the middle of the 20th century.

In June 1974, unusual earthquake activity began in Bárðarbunga. Earthquakes of intensity 5 or above occurred in the caldera rim at regular intervals until 1996. It is still not totally clear what caused these large earthquakes, but they may have been caused by subsidence in Bárðarbunga's caldera. There also appeared to be a strange connection between earthquake activity in Bárðarbunga and volcanic activity at Krafla, over 100 km further north in the volcanic zone. However, these earthquakes ended with a "bang" in 1996 when a large earthquake happened on 29 September. After that, there was a powerful series of earthquakes, unlike previous tremors, and these finally lead to a large eruption in the neighbouring volcanic system, Grímsvötn. Subsequently, the earthquake behaviour at Bárðarbunga changed again, and large tremors ceased for a while. From 2005 onwards, earthquake activity increased again in Bárðarbunga, but diminished once more after another eruption at Grímsvötn in 2011.

Early in the summer of 2014, earthquake activity and tectonic plate movement be-

came noticeable, indicating that magma was rising beneath Bárðarbunga. In the early hours of 16 August 2014 things really got going when a major series of earthquakes began, different from those previously recorded at Bárðarbunga. It was immediately clear that magma movement was taking place beneath the central volcano, and in the first 24 hours, the magma managed to break its way southeast from the Bárðarbunga volcano. With the help of seismometers, an exceptionally good picture was obtained of these magma movements, showing how the earthquakes arranged themselves on an increasingly long line out from Bárðarbunga. This was thought to be clear evidence of the formation of a magmatic intrusion, an underground channelling of magma along what is called a dyke. In the area around Bárðarbunga there are many very accurate GPS-stations that register small movements on the earth's crust. At the start of the activity, while the magma was breaking its way out from Bárðarbunga, most of the GPS-stations moved rapidly away from the dyke, at right-angles to the dyke's path at any given time. This was a clear indication that a large volume of magma was being intruded along the dyke. As the dyke continued to lengthen, however, the GPS-stations stopped moving away from it, and began to do the opposite. The GPS-stations started to move towards Bárðarbunga volcano, indicating that magma was flowing out from the volcano and the magma chamber deep beneath it was contracting. Eventually, radar measurements made by satellite, InSAR measurements, proved very helpful. Such measurements have shown how the land surface around Bárðarbunga rose and fell while the volcanic activity occurred.

In late August 2014, earth scientists could do little other than monitor what was happening, and try to predict how it would continue. Probably few expected that events would take the form that they did, but as is usually the case with geologists, no scenario was excluded. The dyke continued to break its way from Bárðarbunga, but soon took a north-easterly direction, beneath Dyngjujökull. Measurements show that several factors determined how the dyke broke its pathway, but it can be assumed that it always took the "easiest" way, where the bedrock offered the least resistance. Closest to Bárðarbunga, the dyke followed the slope of the mountainside, moving towards lower overburden of rock and glacial ice. But at an increased distance from the volcano, variations in crustal tension directed the dyke towards the northeast, parallel to the direction of the rift zone. What particularly surprised scientists regarding the formation of the dyke, was that magma from Bárðarbunga seemed to be forcing its way into the Askja volcanic system – this is thought to extend south from Dyngjufjöll, towards Dyngjujökull. So the events led to a reassessment of the orientation of the volcanic systems, because it seems that Bárðarbunga and Askja interact north of the icecap, where their volcanic systems meet. At the end of August, magma finally reached the surface, first in a small eruption on 29 August, and then on 31 August a large fissure eruption began. There was already a small lava field where the eruption occurred, thought to be between 140 and 200 years old. It was called Holuhraun, and so was the new eruption.

The lava eruption at Holuhraun proved to be much larger in most respects than anyone anticipated. Right from the first few days of the eruption, its power was evident when it spread very quickly down to the braided stream bed of Jökulsá á Fjöllum, where the river emerges from beneath Dyngjujökull, close to the eruption site. The eruption began on a 1500 m long fissure, but fairly quickly it became restricted to a few large craters from which the lava flooded downhill, mainly to the northwest and east, as conditions allowed. Comprehensive measurements of the lava were made in mid-Jan-

uary 2015, and it was discovered that the lava was about 30–40 m thick closest to the eruption site, and 20–25 m thick in most places. By December the lava had spread across an area of 80 km^2, but it stopped advancing after that, and the lava field mostly just became thicker until the eruption ended in February. Around mid-January, the volume of lava was estimated at about 1.4 km^3, making it the largest lava eruption since Eldhraun was erupted from the Laki crater row in 1783–84, although Holuhraun was actually only one-tenth of Eldhraun's volume. Dreadful air pollution accompanied the eruption, and a blue haze lay for weeks across northeast and east Iceland, much to the dismay of the inhabitants.

At the same time, the glacier above Bárðarbunga's caldera subsided by tens of metres. There were no indications that the subsidence was caused by glacial melting, so there is no doubt that major subsidence of the caldera floor occurred. When an event like this occurs in the summit caldera of a volcano, it is called caldera collapse, and the last event of this type in Iceland happened at Askja in the Dyngjufjöll mountain group, after the explosive eruption there in 1875.That event, however, was much more extreme than the caldera collapse in Bárðarbunga. Scientists attempted to predict the end of the eruption by projecting the subsidence rate of Bárðarbunga's caldera. Both the subsidence rate and the lava flow rate gradually declined over time, and it was assumed that when the subsidence stopped, the volcanic activity would cease. This proved to be the case at the end of February 2015 when the eruption ended and subsidence in Bárðarbunga had virtually ceased. The eruption had lasted about six months, and an enormous expanse of lava had formed at Holuhraun, about 85 km^2 in area.

Data that was collected during the eruption will be used for research for a long time, decades even. Several scientific articles about the events have already been published, especially analysing the intrusion of the dyke, included in the journal *Nature*. A detailed geochemical analysis of the new lava is yet to be published, but it is clear that the magma belonged to the Bárðarbunga volcanic system, and not to the Askja system. Further chemical analysis will probably better define ideas about the magma's origin, its evolution and its journey to the surface. In addition to direct measurement and analysis of the eruption, many interesting speculations arise in connection with the event. It would be interesting, for example, to calculate how large a flood (jökulhlaup) could have occurred if an eruption of this size had happened beneath Dyngjujökull where the glacier is up to 500-600 m thick.

At the time of this book's publication in the spring of 2016, about a year after the Holuhraun eruption ended, it is clear that magma has already collected again beneath the Bárðarbunga central volcano. So it is possible that this series of volcanic events is not yet over, and it will be exciting to watch the Bárðarbunga system in the coming years. Holuhraun itself is still very hot, quite unique and intriguing. In the summer of 2015, a hiking trail was marked around the lava's edge, although no actual path has been laid. The trail is consequently very difficult; the lava is extremely rough and unsuitable for inexperienced hikers. This should not, however, prevent people from going into the highlands and enjoying the latest addition to Iceland's geology.

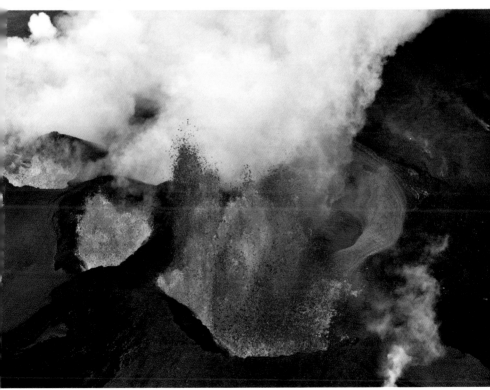

Askja in the Dyngjufjöll mountains

Askja, in the Dyngjufjöll mountain group, is a very bleak place. Because of its location in the highlands north of Vatnajökull icecap, few people go there, and the majority of those who do are foreign tourists. It could be said that Askja is shrouded in mystery related to violent and disturbing events that took place there after Icelanders first encountered the force of the area. Askja was given protected status as a natural monument in 1978, and it has been under the auspices of Vatnajökull National Park since 2009. On the eastern outskirts of Dyngjufjöll stands the highland centre at Drekagil. The Touring Club of Akureyri first erected a mountain hut there in 1968. A road leads from Drekagil to a car park at Askja, and it is a half-hour walk from there to Víti and Öskjuvatn, two lakes inside the caldera.

Askja is one of the best known volcanoes in the country. It lies in the middle of a large mountain range, Dyngjufjöll, named after Kollóttadyngja, the lava shield just north of the mountains. Askja is a central volcano, a volcano that has built up by repeated eruptions over a long time period. Askja's eruption history doubtless extends back a few thousand years before glaciation ended, although the age and development of the volcano's earlier stage are not well understood.

The Dyngjufjöll mountains are the main product of the volcanic activity, and they are largely composed of móberg (hyaloclastite), which formed in eruptions beneath Ice Age glaciers. Few lava flows have been identified from earlier interglacial (warm) periods, but since the Ice Age glaciers vanished around 10,000 years ago, the Askja volcanic system has been very active. Like other places in Iceland, volcanic activity was greatest in the first few thousand years after the end of glaciation – this is the period when most of the enormous lava shields in the volcanic zones were erupted. This great activity can be explained by the retreat of the Ice Age glaciers. It removed a huge load from the crust, resulting in increased magma production beneath the country.

In many people's minds, Askja is probably best known for an enormous explosive eruption that occurred there in 1875, but that was not the volcano's largest known eruption. The first signs of activity at Askja from the end of glaciation are the extensive tephra (ash and pumice) layers found on many coastlines in northern Iceland, which have been traced to Dyngjufjöll. The thickness and distribution of the tephra layers indicate that a large explosive eruption occurred inside the central volcano, and it has been es-

timated to be 5-10 times larger than the 1875 explosive eruption. Askja's eruption history is complicated though, and it has been difficult to unequivocally connect this explosive eruption with a particular location in Dyngjufjöll. Volcanic activity gradually decreased over time, and the first thousand years after Iceland's settlement, little of note seems to have occurred in the Dyngjufjöll mountains. No doubt lightening was seen from time to time, up in the highlands, but few would have bothered to investigate the site of any eruptions - it was far to travel and foolish to waste any effort exploring natural disasters like these. Consequently, the Icelandic public did not really become aware of Askja until the second half of the 19th century.

In 1874 a major series of eruptions began in the volcano, climaxing in a large explosive eruption. The earthquakes began early in 1874 when a large eruption cloud was seen rising above the Dyngjufjöll mountains. Later in the year, earthquakes became noticeable and fissures opened south of the main route between Mývatn and Hólsfjöll, at a place called Sveinagjá. On 1 January 1875, an eruption cloud rose above the highlands north of Vatnajökull, and two days later an eruption could be seen close to Askja. In February, a group of local men from Mývatn went south to Dyngjufjöll and described the turmoil frightening hot spring activity and friable ground, and: considerable subsidence in the southeast corner of the caldera. At the same time, people noticed an eruption at Sveinagjá, but when the area was investigated a few days later the eruption was over. Sveinagjá erupted again in early March, and that eruption ended just before something more serious took place. In the evening of 28 March, an eruption cloud was seen rising from Askja, and that night an enormous explosive eruption began. Tephra fell for six hours, from dawn onwards, and a thick layer of ash fell over an area at least 150 km wide,

northeast from Askja and reaching to the coast. In this eruption, the explosion crater Víti was formed, and for many years it was thought to be the source of the main explosive eruption came from it. It has since become clear that the main craters were where Lake Öskjuvatn now stands, and that Víti was formed in large explosions at the end of the eruption, when magma encountered groundwater in the area. Quite a number of eruptions happened at Sveinagjá in April, August and October the same year, and then this series of eruptions ended.

The eruption history of Askja did not end with the large 1875 event, however. A few eruptions occurred there between 1921 and 1929. They formed, among other things, both the island Askur or Hornfirðingahólmi in the southern part of the lake, and the small lava flow on the slopes of Dyngjufjöll above Víti, called Bátshraun. In 1961 an eruption began again; this time close to the gap in the caldera rim. This area is now called Vikraborgir, and fairly large scoria cones formed in the eruption and lava flowed out of the caldera gap. The lava is called Vikrahraun.

Although the explosive eruption in March 1875 was very short, it caused a large ash fall over the whole of northeast Iceland, and ash was carried all the way to Scandinavia. The ash fall was worst for the farming area on Jökuldalsheiði, between the Jökuldalur valley and the mountains of Möðrudalsfjallgarður. After the eruption, farms were abandoned temporarily or for longer, and the rural district never properly recovered. Even though emigration from Iceland to North America had begun quite a while before the 1875 Askja eruption, the disaster gave impetus to the stream of people heading westwards across the ocean. But the disaster also encouraged foreign geologists' interest in Icelandic volcanoes, and quite a few scientists came to Iceland to study the after-effects of the explosive eruption. We have a fairly good idea of the events and their aftermath, even though the story is not at all simple. Before the event in 1874-75, the caldera now occupied by Lake Öskjuvatn did not exist. It was created in its present form over a fairly long period following the explosive eruption. The first signs of a graben were seen when the men from Mývatn explored the area in February 1875, shortly before the big eruption. The area was explored occasionally after that, and by 1910, subsidence in the caldera was finally judged to have ended, and Öskjuvatn was fully formed, more or less. The caldera is well over 200 m, and when Sigurjón Rist measured Öskjuvatn in 1963 it proved to be 220 m deep, at its deepest. Newer measurements actually indicate that the lake is even deeper. The volume of the caldera is thought to be about 2-2.5 km^3, but the volume of pumice and ash that were erupted in 1875 is equivalent to only 0.2 km^3 of rock. So the subsidence of the caldera is only partly the result of the explosive eruption itself. Most people think that the caldera was largely, or almost entirely, created when magma from a magma chamber beneath the Dyngjufjöll mountains travelled northwards underground, towards Sveinagjá, where an eruption was also taking place. This is thought to be similar to events seen in the Krafla Fires of the 1970s and ´80s, and in the Bárðarbunga system when an eruption took place north of Vatnajökull in the autumn of 2014. As soon as Askja's magma chamber was emptied by the movement of magma, the ground above it collapsed and the vast graben formed.

The caldera that formed towards the end of the 19th century is, however, only one of three or four separate calderas in the Dyngjufjöll mountains. Only two of these calderas can be readily seen on maps and aerial photographs, the others are largely filled by lavas and are difficult to make out. The main caldera, the great circular graben in the middle of the Dyngjufjöll mountains, is a complicated structure and it is not clear how it formed. It is about 7-8 km in diameter, and possibly formed over a long period after the end of glaciation. When it formed, caldera subsidence probably occurred with or without eruptions from the volcano. The third caldera is the oldest, and it has been named Norðuraskja, and it lies north of the main caldera. It is thought to have formed late in the last glacial period, possibly the result of the large explosive eruption at the end of the last glaciation that was previously mentioned. Over time, the Norðuraskja caldera has been filled by lava, so its floor lies much higher than the floor of the main caldera. The fourth caldera is an indistinct caldera formation near to the gap in the main caldera rim; it is seen as a big subsided area in the eastern part of Dyngjufjöll. It has not been possible to determine its age relative to that of the main caldera.

As readers will doubtless appreciate, the geology of Askja has a lot to offer, and many things are worth looking at when it is visited. In fact, a visit to the kingdom of Askja could be said to begin even before reaching the Dyngjufjöll mountains, because the first signs of the enormous disaster of 1875 are seen when driving onto the thick, snow-white areas of pumice that came from the eruption. The huts at Drekagil were erected on the pumice wasteland, and it is very desolate all around. The view over the barren land is terrific if from the top of one of the many peaks in the area. From Dreki it is possible to drive through the caldera gap to Vikraborgir, where the road ends. From Vikraborgir it is about a 30-40 minute walk to Víti and Öskjuvatn, on a relatively level trail. Even in poor weather the walk from the car park is worth the effort, and perhaps the experience is appreciated even more in worse weather. Víti should be examined first - the cliff walls of the crater are complex and the colours of the water and cliffs are glorious. It has been popular to descend into Víti to bathe, but this is frequently impossible because of snow accumulated on the crater slopes. Öskjuvatn is a complete contrast to Víti, deep blue and cold. On the far side of the lake are signs of an enormous landslip that occurred in 2014. To the left are the Bátshraun lava and its craters, high on the caldera side. Inside the caldera, white pumice alternates with jet-black material from the older and younger lava eruptions. Because the great explosive eruption of 1875 took place in the middle of winter, the pumice fell widely on thick snow-drifts, so in some places it is possible to find 140-year-old snow under the pumice.

But it is not just the caldera that is worth visiting. In the eastern part of Dyngjufjöll, near to the Dreki highland centre, there are several beautiful geological localities. Next to the Dreki huts, the Drekagil gully cuts deep into the mountains. A path has been made about 400–500 m into the gully, leading to beautiful waterfalls, but on the way some excellent pillow lavas can be seen, and lots of móberg (hyaloclastite). Just south of Dreki is another exceptional geological site, called Nautagil. Nautagil is interestingly connected to the space race of the 20th century. American astronauts from NASA came on training courses to Iceland in 1965 and '67. In both cases they went into Askja and spent time there doing geological exercises under the guidance of two Icelandic geologists, Sigurður Þórarinsson and Guðmundur Sigvaldason. One of the places that the groups went to was Nautagil, which was named after them – a shortened version of Astrónautagil. In Nautagil there is a big heap of pumice from the 1875 explosive eruption, but the most interesting things are the large and impressive columnar jointed formations that look like enormous flowers, high on the right-hand side of the gully as you enter.

Those who visit Askja can hardly avoid feeling fear-tinged respect for it. Nobody should approach the volcano without studying the tragic story of Ina von Grumbkow, who visited it in 1908. Her story, and that of Walter von Knebel, her geologist fiancé, is particularly gloomy. He and his companion disappeared in a mysterious manner while doing geological research on Lake Öskjuvatn in 1907. Ina came to Iceland searching for news of him, but found nothing. She erected a cairn on the shore of Öskjuvatn in memory of him, and no visit to Askja is complete without looking at the cairn. Askja is undoubtedly among the most amazing places in the highlands, and the rugged, desolate landscape within the vast caldera is virtually unparalleled anywhere in the world.

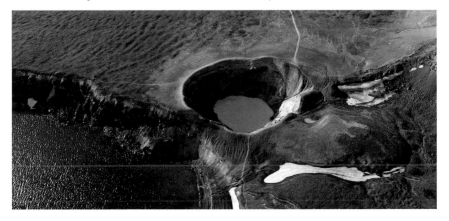

Herðubreið

Herðubreið has frequently been called the Queen of Icelandic Mountains. It holds an important place in the hearts of many Icelanders and was actually voted "National Mountain" in an informal poll in 2002. Herðubreið is visible from many places in the highlands north of Vatnajökull. The view of the mountain from Möðrudalur is thought particularly beautiful; Möðrudalur was the home of father-and-son artists Jón Stefánsson and Stefán Jónsson who immortalised Herðubreið in their paintings. Herðubreið was first climbed officially in 1908 by German geologist Hans Reck and Icelander Sigurður Sumarliðason. Actually, an American adventurer, William Lee Howard, said that he had climbed the mountain when he visited Iceland thirty years earlier, and the story of his journey was published in 1881 in the New York Tribune. Howard said that he was 38 hours on the way to the top, and used a kite to attach a climbing rope to the mountainside before hauling himself up. It goes without saying that few people have paid much attention to this tall story, but Howard was probably first to assert that Herðubreið was a volcano. Scientists did not generally believe that until Hans and Sigurður described the summit crater on the mountain after their climb in 1908.

So Herðubreið is a volcano, but unlike the great central volcanoes in the country, Askja and Krafla for example, Herðubreið was probably formed in a single eruption, although suggestions have been made that it formed in several eruptions, over a long time. Usually, however, it is taken as an example of a volcano that erupted only once, which is probably the case for most volcanoes in Iceland, apart from the central volcanoes. Such volcanoes are often called monogenetic, indicating that their history has only one "generation". Consequently, we need not worry too much about an eruption in Herðubreið – it is not seen as an active volcano.

Age-dating indicates that Herðubreið formed about 10,000-11,000 years ago, just before the end of glaciation, and the eruption occurred beneath a thick Ice Age glacier. In a subglacial eruption, volcanic material piles up and forms a mountain instead of spreading out as it does in a lava eruption on ice-free land. When magma first erupts under the base of a glacier, it comes into contact with cold meltwater. The magma is suddenly chilled by this, and one of two things can happen. If the pressure of the overlying glacier is high, the magma can flow out of the vent and form what is called pillow lava. However, at lower pressures closer to the glacier surface, the magma is torn apart in an explosive ash-forming eruption and becomes shards of volcanic glass (hyaloclastite) that later become hard móberg (palagonite tuff). In subglacial eruptions, pillow lavas are often erupted first, building up into a mound. As the volcanic vent moves closer to the glacier surface, the eruption changes to a new phase and ash is produced in an explosive eruption. The ash piles up on top of the pillow lavas, and forms a small hill of hyaloclastite. If the eruption lasts a long time, it moves into a third phase when the vent reaches the top of the glacier and meltwater no longer has easy access to the crater. Explosive activity stops then, and lava flows from the crater instead. In this final phase a lava cap is formed on the mountain, and this type of mountain is called a tuya, or table mountain. Herðubreið is a good example of a tuya.

The summit of Herðubreið is 1682 m above sea level, and the surrounding highland plateau is about 1100 m lower. So the height from the plateau up to cliffs at the base of Herðubreið's lava cap is about 400-600 m. Since the lava cap first began to form when the eruption had emerged from the glacier, the height of the lower part of the mountain provides some clue as to the thickness of the glacier in this region when Herðubreið erupted - it was close to 1000 m thick. However, this does not tell us everything about the maximum thickness of the Ice Age glacier because the ice was already thinning when the eruption occurred, and in fact the glacier in the highlands was probably between one and two kilometres thick when the Ice Age reached its maximum.

There is one ascent route for Herðubreið, and it is usually open for experienced hikers, although it is sometimes difficult in early summer because of snow. A risk of falling rocks means that a safety helmet should always be worn when climbing the mountain, and crampons and an ice axe are also necessary if there is a lot of snow. When the top of Herðubreið is reached, the lovely circular summit crater can be seen - half-full of water and with a frozen surface well into the summer. Around the crater is a thick heap of lava, weathered and fractured, and from the top there is a panoramic view across north and northeast Iceland. From below, it is difficult to see how Herðubreið's summit looks, and most people thought that it was covered by a glacier until Hans and Sigurður made the ascent in 1908 and corrected this misconception. In the aforementioned interview with William Lee Howard, from 1881, he stated that the top was covered with lava, and that it must be a volcano, even though he did not mention a summit crater. Howard's description of the structure of Herðubreið is so close to the truth that the question must arise: did he in fact ascend the mountain after all? Did he perhaps get carried away by a habitual tendency to exaggerate, and change his description of a perfectly normal mountain climb into fantasy, so that no one believed that he really made it to the top?

Sources

Material for this book was largely derived from peer-reviewed literature, both international and Icelandic journals, and other academic literature and reference books about Iceland's geology. A comprehensive list of more than 450 references in Icelandic and English can be found in the Icelandic version of this book, *Vegvísir um jarðfræði Íslands*, which was published in June 2015. Of these references, about half are in Icelandic, but more specialised geological articles in peer-reviewed journals, postgraduate theses and scientific reports are usually in English.

Two magazines about natural history and geology are published in Iceland. The natural history periodical *Náttúrufræðingurinn* has been published since 1931; most of the articles are in Icelandic, but there is usually a short summary in English. The Icelandic journal of earth sciences, *Jökull*, which has been published since 1951, has almost always been in English, and it is recommended as reference material for readers of this book. Issue 58 of *Jökull*, which came out in 2008, is particularly recommended because it was a Special Issue, containing themed papers providing an overview of the geology of Iceland, written by the country's leading earth scientists. It includes review articles on crustal movements, glaciers, geothermal systems, volcanic activity and volcanic hazards in Iceland.

In addition to the above sources, a range of geological maps published in Iceland were consulted during the writing of this book. These include a geological map for the whole of Iceland (1:600 000) from the Icelandic Institute of Natural History, showing the main features of bedrock, and more detailed geological maps of North and Southwest Iceland (1:100 000) published by Iceland GeoSurvey (ÍSOR).